ANGELS
OVER KISANGANI

They Wrestled Not Against
Flesh and Blood

ABIGAIL DUMAN

Pacific Press®
Publishing Association
Nampa, Idaho | www.pacificpress.com

Cover design by Gerald Lee Monks
Cover design resources provided by the author
Interior photos provided by the author
Inside design by Aaron Troia

The author assumes full responsibility for the accuracy of all facts and quotations as cited in this book.

Additional copies of this book are available for purchase by calling toll-free 1-800-765-6955 or by visiting AdventistBookCenter.com.

Library of Congress Cataloging-in-Publication Data
Names: Duman, Abigail, 1994- author.
Title: Angels over Kisangani : they wrestled not against flesh and blood / Abigail Duman.
Description: Nampa : Pacific Press Publishing Association, 2021. |
    Summary: "The true story of missionaries in Congo and their life-threatening
    encounters"—Provided by publisher.
Identifiers: LCCN 2021032762 (print) | LCCN 2021032763 (ebook) |
    ISBN 9780816367740 (paperback) | ISBN 9780816367757 (ebook)
Subjects: LCSH: Missions—Congo (Democratic Republic) | Missionaries—Congo
    (Democratic Republic) | Seventh-day Adventists—Missions—Congo
    (Democratic Republic)
Classification: LCC BV3625.C6 D77 2021 (print) | LCC BV3625.C6 (ebook) |
    DDC 266.676751—dc23
LC record available at https://lccn.loc.gov/2021032762
LC ebook record available at https://lccn.loc.gov/2021032763ISBN 978-0-8163-6774-0

August 2021

CONTENTS

PREFACE

When James Calvert—an early missionary to the cannibals of Fiji—embarked on his missionary journey in 1838, the ship captain tried to turn him back by saying, "You will lose your life and lives of those with you if you go among such savages."[1]

To this, Calvert replied, "We died before we came here."[2]

Death to self places individuals where God can use them the most. It takes them to an experience where the fear of God is greater than that of man. Missionary Keith Mosier told me that one day, in the humid tropical woodlands of the Democratic Republic of Congo. As a fellow missionary, I saw, through the series of events recorded in this account, how right he was.

When my husband, Christopher, and I first arrived in the Democratic Republic of Congo (DRC) in January 2016, we were unseasoned and largely ignorant of Congolese culture and history. Little did we realize that this mission field was actually dangerous—for obvious and not-so-obvious reasons. However, being convicted that the Lord had led us there and being willing to take risks for His sake, we embarked on a process of surrender and death to self that prepared the way for us to experience faith in the face of ultimate fear.

Every story of God's power to save is worth retelling, but this one is special for me to share because I was there to see it. I saw the clash between the powers of light and darkness, good and evil, love and hate. I saw God's power manifested in a dusty, far-removed city called Kisangani.

---

1. John Calvert quoted by Teanna Sunberg, "The Beautiful and Messy Call of a Missionary," *Holiness Today*, January/February 2018, https://www.holinesstoday.org/the-beautiful-and-messy-call-of-a-missionary.

2. Sunberg, "Beautiful and Messy Call."

CHAPTER 1

AN UNLIKELY CALLING

A brilliant sun sent piercing beams of light through the dense jungle canopy as the Congo Frontline Mission (CFM) campus awakened to a new day. An African grey parrot cackled from the fronds of a tall date nut palm just as several Congolese men rounded a corner on the gravel road below. Without slowing their pace, they tramped over a black trail of army ants as thick as a snake.

"It's a peaceful day, Mamma* Rebecca!" a slender man with defined cheekbones and close-cropped hair called out to a woman in her pineapple garden.

"It is indeed, Kayumba!" She paused to rest on the wooden handle of her homemade hoe. Rebecca's umber eyes sparkled in the morning sunlight as she watched the jovial group pass by.

The men were in good spirits as they approached a familiar porch and waited respectfully on the hand-cut grass. At the age of thirty-five, Kayumba had an extended history of employment by the mission, which made him the unspoken leader. He climbed the few small cement steps to the porch, paused, and listened.

On that morning, even the deaf man in the nearby village of Huit could not have denied that the Mosier missionary family was alive and well.

"Anna, Jesus wants you to be a happy girl and to eat your breakfast this morning." The gentle voice of Keith Mosier spoke above the sudden clanging of a metal pan lid as it journeyed from the table to the cement floor. "Are you going to choose to be a happy girl?"

Two-year-old Anna Mosier tilted her head full of blond curls and pouted, eyeing her four-year-old brother Caleb as he helped himself to a plain glass jar of freshly processed peanut butter.

"OK, I'll take you to your room, and you can come out again when you decide to be Daddy's happy girl." Keith lifted her up from a small wooden chair and took her hand in his.

---

* Mamma is a courteous Congolese term for a married woman.

Kayumba coughed discreetly on the porch.

"Good morning Kayumba!" Keith flashed an upbeat grin through the screened window as a long lizard darted behind polyester curtains adorned with a local print. "I will be right with you," Keith said in fluent Swahili.

"*Sawa* [OK]," Kayumba replied, nodding.

After placing Anna in her room to contemplate her attitude, Keith again sat down at the table. He looked lovingly at his wife, Tammy, who was feeding their toddler Talitha in her highchair. "God has blessed us so much as a family. Would you please pass me the honey, Caleb?"

Caleb dutifully obeyed. Then the door to Anna's bedroom opened, and a jubilant little figure in a pink dress burst into the living room. "I'm a happy girl now!" The girl smiled, and her tight curls bounced as she marched forward with her arms extended for a hug.

"I'm so glad to see that." Keith's tones were warm but mixed with tenors of strength and purpose. He pushed his chair back and welcomed his chubby cherub to the table warmly. "You have plenty of oatmeal here in your bowl, and we have honey that Daddy brought back from Tanzania last December."

Hardly had Anna been seated before she began to vigorously rub her eyes. Blinking for a moment before refocusing, she stared down at her plate with a disconsolate expression.

Tammy seemed to sense an upcoming repeat of the last five minutes. "I wonder if she managed to get into the peanuts again. What an unfortunate item to be allergic to here in Congo."

"Yes, she did, Mamma," six-year-old Shiloh stated matter-of-factly from her seat at the table. "I think Grandma fed her *sombeii** with peanuts by mistake."

"Oh, I'm so sorry." Alvina Rittenour, a slim woman with dark hair and glasses, paused at the kitchen sink. "I didn't realize that Mamma Nikke made two different batches of greens—with and without peanuts—yesterday."

"This is not the first time that Anna has had peanuts accidentally," Tammy reassured her mother.

Keith met the men waiting outside and absentmindedly ran a hand through his thick brown hair. Before any further discussion, he inquired about the men's welfare. Then, when the culturally expected greetings came to a close, Keith laid out the day's plan. "Today, we need to work on drilling a well just off campus for the children at the school," he explained. "You can report to Nathan for more details. I should be at the office building most of the day if anyone needs me."

Nathan Rittenour, Keith's brother-in-law and neighbor on the campus

---

* *Sombeii* is made of pounded cassava leaf doused in oil and sometimes mixed with peanuts.

property, took the primary responsibility for the mission's well-drilling projects. With contaminated water being a chief reason for health issues in Congo, Nathan was never short of inspiration for his efforts to bring clean water to its people.

The group of Congolese mission workers passed Mamma Rebecca again as they relocated, loitering this time by the Rittenour porch. Mamma Rebecca was perched on a sturdy stool made of dried vines, surrounded by bar soap and bright blue water basins, and sang softly as her dark, calloused hands scrubbed American clothes.

"Take the name of Jesus with you,
Child of sorrow and of woe . . .
Precious name, O how sweet!
Hope of earth and joy of heaven."[1]

Nathan bounded from his doorway with a broad-brimmed hat and a contemplative expression that rarely left his face. Inside, his wife, Starla, combed through her thick, jet-black hair and laughed as she watched their fair, good-natured son, Daniel, bounce on "Stubby"—an inflated horse made of blue plastic. The couple brought the horse for Daniel to pass the time on well drilling trips, "bouncing" in the vehicle as his father drilled and sweated under the tropical sun.

Both Mosier and Rittenour couples were in their late twenties to mid thirties. While both families were visionaries with the same common goal—to bring the gospel to Congo—their similarities and differences were striking to any curious observer.

Keith Mosier's persona was marked with energy and optimism: a motivational glow seemed to travel with him wherever he went, breathing life into all that made the campus vibrant and productive. Having moved to Tanzania as a teenager, he spoke Swahili fluently and had an unwavering love for Africa. He lived each day in this massive continent ever hopeful and ever dreaming of a brighter future for the people he desired to reach with the message of redemption.

The Mosiers were one of the first American families to establish themselves in Congo after a long African civil war came to a close in the early 2000s. At the time, there were no other European foreigners for three hundred miles. Roads leading to and from Kisangani were impassable, so any necessary supplies had to be purchased locally or flown in by plane from more flourishing areas of Congo. When Keith, backed by the newly established Congo Frontline Mission, purchased a piece of raw land several miles outside the city, the jungle was next to impenetrable. The young man found the thickets so dense that he was forced to crawl on his hands and knees to explore its boundaries.

How could his small team build a school for evangelism and make this land their home? Keith was undaunted. With positivity and determination, he introduced a bulldozer to the undeveloped, untamed property. His team soon discovered large termite mounds (good for making bricks), gravel, and sand for building. The campus quickly began taking shape. By 2017, there were more than fourteen buildings, a circle of lovingly planted young date palms around the campus green, and many families who called the place home.

Keith's vision eclipsed not only the immediate challenges at hand but also Congo's ever-threatening political turmoil. Year after year, sitting Congolese President Joseph Kabila delayed the vote for a change of leadership. At the close of each year (when the vote was repeatedly delayed), a tide of skirmishes broke out between police, rebels, and protesting locals across the country. Residents were forced to lie low and bide their time. Tensions swelled on all sides, with the Catholic church being a powerful voice against government control.

During the uncertain election seasons, Keith took his family on road trips out of the country for their safety. Recently, he had traveled to familiar territory in Tanzania. Once there, Keith booked a ferry from the bustling city of Dar es Salaam to the tropical island of Zanzibar. He found an inexpensive room on a desolate beach and splashed through the foaming green waves with his little following of blond children. All the while, Keith wondered if Congo would slip over the brink into widespread violence. Though he smiled and laughed with his children as if without a care in the world, his heart was never far from the people who remained behind with an uncertain future.

Both Keith and Tammy Mosier were adventurous. They each felt called to labor in Congo in young adulthood. As a young woman, Tammy wanted to find the neediest, spiritually darkest place on the globe to serve God, and she found it in Congo—named by London-based charity Save the Children as the worst country in the world to be a mother in 2013.

Congo was surely a place for the called—the risks to personal health and safety were too great otherwise. Cutthroat thieves, greedy government officials, rampant tropical disease, and poor health care were only a few of the hazards the missionaries faced. But in the cool of the evening, as Keith put-putted around the campus on his motorcycle with three beaming children holding on for dear life, Congo felt safe. Adventist worker families emerged from their humble homes on the campus, full of smiles and pleasant greetings for their leader and his family.

AN UNLIKELY CALLING

Nathan Rittenour and his wife, Starla, felt just as called by God to come to this country but lived more cautiously than their relatives. "Living in Congo is enough of a risk," Starla was known to say. "No need to take unnecessary ones." Deep in the jungle interior, while on a well-drilling trip, their only child, Daniel, had almost died of pneumonia. Ever since the near-tragedy, they carefully watched the little boy for respiratory struggles. Starla rarely traveled by motorcycle, much less allowed Daniel to ride behind Nathan on the popular Congolese transportation vehicle.

In a clearing beyond the Rittenour home was a newly built structure where the Dumans lived. Their house was nestled on two sides by oil palms and a jungle canopy where birds rarely ceased their singing. Decorative bricks allowed air to flow in through the eaves of the metal roof. The newcomer missionaries, Christopher and Abigail Duman, learned that window screens were a rare luxury in this place. However, they soon found that even screened windows never seemed to keep out ferocious mosquitoes or slithering lizards.

"Have a good day," Abigail waved to her husband as he set off on foot for the Rittenour home that bright morning. "Don't forget to come back for lunch!"

Watching the figure of her young husband disappear around the bend, she smiled wistfully. *He loves it here*, she thought. *If it were up to him, I don't think he would ever leave.*

The Dumans were by far the greenest missionary couple on campus. They arrived in Kisangani largely ignorant of the history, culture, and language of the country they were about to be immersed in, but circumstances leading to their stay in Congo were so providential that the couple never doubted their mission.

Only a few months earlier, as Christopher drove on a country road in Alabama, Abigail broached the topic, explaining that foreign missions were a dream close to her heart.

Christopher made it clear that such a venture would be close to impossible. "Abigail, we own a house, pay on a car, and have two cats and a dog," he reminded his twenty-two-year-old wife of two years. "It's difficult for me to take several weeks of vacation off from my work, much less months. I know that God doesn't want us to be irresponsible. I don't see how we could leave for any significant amount of time."

Abigail took a deep breath. "If it's God's will, He can arrange everything. My question is, would you be willing?"

The twenty-five-year-old paused in the driver's seat, still looking skeptical. Finally, he said, "It would be next to impossible, but yes, if God opened a door and called, I would be willing to go."

"That's all He needs to hear." His wife looked businesslike as a satisfied smile curled across her face; she folded her hands in her lap and straightened her shoulders. "Our willingness is all that He asks for."

One week later, to the day, Christopher received a text message alert and reached for his cell phone to read it. He stared solemnly at the screen. "Chris," he read the message aloud and slowly digested each word. "Would you and Abigail consider doing mission work if someone paid all of your bills and trip expenses?" The text message had come from his employer.

Abigail's eyes brightened with amazement and hope. For her, that one text message spelled out the fulfillment of a dream to risk something for heaven. God had not forgotten her childhood prayers.

"Let me call for more details," Christopher cautioned. "I don't know what this means."

The story quickly unfolded. "My wife and I were looking to buy a larger house, one better suited to our business," the man explained. "We prayed and asked that God would open or close doors according to His will. I stepped forward to buy the place we were wanting, but it had just gone under contract." He paused. "When Jesus comes, I don't want Him to find me sitting over a pile of money, waiting to buy myself a bigger house."

After taking a deep breath, he continued. "I know that we haven't talked about this before, but this has been on my heart for several months. My family and I are willing to cover every bill during your time of absence—from your electric payment to your dog food. Various issues keep me from being able to go myself," he said. "But you are young and in good health, and we would like to know that we made it possible for others to go in our place."

Christopher set the phone down in astonishment as Abigail sank to her knees on the floor and searched his face. "Is this not an open door?" she asked.

A broad grin spread across his face. "It would seem so."

"I feel very touched," his young wife said, seeking to express herself. "God has not forgotten me. How awesome that God Himself makes His will so perfectly clear to two people out of earth's billions!"

A few months later, the Dumans found themselves in Congo.

On this particular day, Abigail blinked in the morning sunlight, standing on the cement porch of her Congo home. Nathan, Christopher, Kayumba, and several other men in a heavy Fuso truck roared past on the gravel road. It was a new day, a fresh opportunity to make a difference in the world.

The Mosier, Rittenour, and Duman families, joined by Tanzanian-born Msifiri and Mamma Mtenzi, determined to carry a flicker of light into Congo's spiritual darkness. Most of the families in the relatively small band had mission experience, even though the Dumans were fresh from the States. And, together on the campus property, they were a team—they were a family—committed to bringing love to a broken and desperate people who longed for change after years of hatred and war. A daunting mission? Yes, for more reasons than the mission team could understand. An unlikely calling? Maybe. But nevertheless, it was a reality. A reality because when God called, a few families said, "Yes, we will take a risk for the gospel."

---

1. Lillian Baxter, "Take the Name of Jesus With You" (1870).

CHAPTER 2

ANGELS AND WITCHES

The Fuso sputtered and bumped across ruts in the road and finally pulled into the schoolyard. Students—some the children of Adventist workers living on campus and others from nearby Huit village—scrambled from their desks and ran to peer through the glass windows of the one-room schoolhouse.

Mamma Rose, her pleasant oval face glowing from an early morning scrub at the river, joined her students at the window. Her toddler babbled from the corner of the room, where he sat on a clean but worn blanket.

"What are they doing, teacher?" a curious student from Huit inquired.

"They are drilling a well for us," Mamma Rose answered, smiling. "Won't it be wonderful to have clean water to drink so close by?"

Soon, the small well-drilling rig was clanking and rumbling on a small mound, surrounded by muck and water sitting in pools. Chris crouched in the mud, studying a sample of gravel in his hand. "So, this is what the ground looks like twenty feet below."

Several uneventful hours passed. "The machine is running smoothly," Nathan shouted above the noise of the rig. His characteristically quiet voice strained to be heard. "I'm going back to campus for a few minutes. Kayumba knows the procedure at this point."

Kayumba stood to the side of the machinery. The muscles in his arms bulged as he removed a well-drilling stem. Water spurted into the air like a geyser, thoroughly soaking his dusty clothes.

Bystanders on the dirt road nearby watched the frighteningly glorious machine with curiosity. Many were journeying to Kisangani from their gardens in the bush. Some carried large loads of charcoal chunks for cooking fires, while others carried heavy stalks of bananas and plantains on their bike racks. A Congolese soldier in a sharp blue uniform coolly watched from the back of a passing motorcycle. An AK-47 hung by a strap over his shoulder and shifted with every bump in the road. The soldier's gaze followed the movement of the rig for only a few seconds before he looked away without expression.

Time seemed to stand still for the many locals who lingered, curious and seemingly without time constraints or deadlines. Christopher waved to the curious onlookers from his position on the rig where he controlled the hydraulic levers.

Just then, two motorcycles came into view, approaching each other as they rounded a bend on the rough road. Both drivers absently stared as Kayumba hoisted up another well-drilling stem and another geyser of water gushed.

Suddenly, the well-drilling crew heard the crunch of metal against metal. The two motorcycles and four people lay sprawled on the ground, looking stunned. One passenger reached for his pant leg and lifted it to reveal a red trickle of blood. In a moment, all stumbled up from the cloud of dust to argue about the event.

"Should we check to see if everyone is OK?" Christopher called to his companion.

Kayumba shook his head. "Don't go. They will say it's your fault and ask you for money. I will go." The man's gaze brightened with his last sentence. He eagerly sloshed through the mud and joined the growing crowd of onlookers taking sides on the road.

"Ah ah, it happened this way . . ." An older man who had witnessed the incident hunched over and gripped a stick as he began to trace a map in the dust. "Listen, everyone." He rapped on the sand, obviously annoyed by the commotion at the scene.

The unharmed passenger brushed the dust from his pant legs and straightened amid the hubbub. Looking the moto-taxi over, he saw that the motorcycle's front fork was bent and out of commission. He shrugged and then set off for Kisangani on foot.

On the other hand, the second motorcycle appeared quite functional, and its owner had every intention of continuing to town. The injured passenger mechanically swung his leg over the side behind the driver as the engine whirred back to life.

"Ahh, don't leave without paying for damages!" the driver of the damaged motorcycle croaked and pushed the old man with the stick aside.

Running to keep pace with the departing motorcycle, the disgruntled driver gained a sudden burst of speed and reached for the ignition to jerk the key.

The driver was not new to this trick: he had plenty of experience escaping police traps in town. He turned up the throttle and left the angry man in the dust. Seeing that the excitement had dissipated, the bystanders finally began to disperse. Pushing his motorcycle back down the road toward Huit, the disgusted driver took one last look at the well-drilling rig.

The village of Huit lay just a mile from the mission through the jungle forest. Although the small community seemed peaceful by day, they had earned a reputation for being on the wild side at night. On weekends and holiday nights, the air pulsed with syncopated rhythms from loud parties. For such a small village, Huit had its own violent past. In the turbulent 1960s, an evangelical missionary was murdered here. It's said that his house still stands in Huit today and that his murderer still lives in the community.

Perversions of justice aren't fair, of course, but life has never been fair for the Congolese. When Europeans arrived in the Democratic Republic of Congo (DRC), they quickly realized the vast assortment of natural resources, and the Congolese people were promptly exploited. In the late nineteenth century, King Leopold II of Belgium claimed that he would improve life for the Congolese, but his real goal was to gain wealth. Life became a continuous nightmare for the Congolese, who were forced to work on rubber plantations and tortured if they could not keep up with the incessant demands of the king. The Belgian government finally seized the Congo "Free State" from the unscrupulous monarch in 1908, but the locals were still mistreated by the wealthy Europeans who remained behind. Cities throughout the country flourished (including Kisangani) as Caucasians took up residency in fancy houses and enjoyed relative peace in the aftermath of World War II. However, all the while, the Congolese were segregated and mistreated. Their patience wore thin: they wanted their country back. When the Congolese people eventually gained freedom from Belgium around 1960, it came at a cost: The government was disorganized, and the economy was crippled. When the last of the Europeans crossed over the Congo border, they left behind an impoverished, diseased, and angry people.

A long period of violence and civil unrest finally gave way to relative peace in the early 2000s. As soon as it was safe, Keith Mosier and Msifiri Mtenzi made plans to start a mission station in Kisangani. The village of Huit benefited from the arrival of the Americans. The mission drilled a well in their community, and a small Seventh-day Adventist congregation formed there. Some of the locals surrendered the injustices of the past to God and experienced peace and a spirit of forgiveness, even though others clung to superstition and fear.

No one could deny that Keith Mosier was a kind and good-hearted man, but a residual bitterness remained in the air—bitterness against any appearance of foreign intervention, especially by light-skinned people—even if it made day-to-day life easier.

The afternoon sun beat down on Christopher and his helpers. Kayumba stretched out under a baby palm tree before taking a swig of water from a faded yellow cooking oil container. The Congolese closed his eyes, then squinted one eye open when he felt the American's gaze.

Christopher shook his head and laughed good-naturedly, turning to a campus worker, Joel, beside him. "Kayumba sleeps."

Joel nodded with an understanding smile.

As the schoolyard emptied of playful children and evening shadows crept over the men at work, Christopher and Kayumba hoisted a sack of bentonite powder onto the rig and tossed spare tools into a locked box with a resounding clang.

"No use tempting people to take anything," Christopher remarked as he placed a wooden board over the tool compartment.

That evening he shuffled across his house porch, wet and mud-caked. Once he was clean and dry again, he perched on a stool in the living room and forked down fried potatoes.

"We made it eighty feet below ground. I met with a little trouble near the end, but we are making good progress and hope to be finished by the end of the week."

"That's great," Abigail said eagerly as she absentmindedly rubbed her fingers together.

"What's wrong with your fingers?"

"Oh," she quickly lowered her hands. "They're a little toasted and very sore. I began the peanut roasting process this afternoon and have yet to master the art."

"Ah," he nodded, then continued. "We use the bentonite as both a sanitary seal and a thickener for the well's walls. We don't want a cave-in on the eighty feet of drilling rod." He grimaced.

Although his skin peeled from sunburn and his jeans qualified as the perfect handwashing nightmare, Christopher had a look of satisfaction as he set his plate down with a clatter on the cement floor. "Two of the men on campus will guard the rig tonight under Nathan's orders. They will take turns sleeping and watching."

"I feel a bit nervous to think about just two of them out there on the secluded road to town," his wife admitted.

"Why, because of the thieves?"

She nodded. "Nathan said that the road leading from our campus driveway to Kisangani has grown more desolate in the last year. And Starla told me the other day that the few who remain are afraid to sleep at night because of harassment from thieves."

"Yes, I know," Christopher agreed. "The thieves want the road to stay deserted and difficult to travel."

Due to the road's sharp corners and rare maintenance, drivers of most vehicles were forced to a snail's crawl. As evening shadows crept through the jungle, thieves waving machetes were known to jump in front of nervous motorcyclists. Without the security of other locals living along the roadside to turn to for help, the drivers, forced to escape on foot, were happy to remain unharmed.

The robbers seemed to find sadistic pleasure in spreading terror by demanding money, stealing anything of value, molesting women, and perpetrating violence on the humble villagers who had little defense against AK-47s. So far, robbers had visited dwellings in every direction but not at the CFM campus.

"God has everything under control." Christopher leaned back in his chair. He seemed to sense his wife's uneasiness.

"Sometimes, I wonder if you fear anything," she mused. Her eyes traced the path of a lizard as it scurried beneath their wooden front door into the night air.

Christopher had always been the fearless one in their relationship. In their few short years of marriage, she had never observed him showing anxiety or stress. In fact, he often reminded her that worrying never did anyone much good and that anxiety decreases lifespan.

Christopher's shoulders quivered for a second as he responded, "Spiders. My mom read books to me as a toddler, and I always shivered when I saw the spiders. Still do, in fact."

Abigail giggled, then turned her head to the window where she heard laughter from the front yard. In the gathering darkness, Joel's family sat around a charcoal fire by their thatched hut and took turns scraping every last bite from a cooking pot. The volume of their conversation ebbed and flowed until all finally became silent.

Later, as she lay beside her sleeping husband under their mosquito net, the thoughts of Abigail's heart grew louder. Her mind rewound to the early days of the mission—reflecting on the stories of when Keith Mosier, his brother-in-law Nathan Rittenour, and a few others arrived in Kisangani after the close of the tumultuous wars. More than five million lives had been lost over the previous ten-year period—mostly from disease and starvation.

Mosier, Rittenour, and the others were visionaries, dreaming of a Congo flooded with the gospel of peace and a people waiting for heaven. When they arrived, they rented a house in the city for temporary living quarters and prayed for guidance on how to proceed.

They soon learned that demonic witchcraft is a powerful reality for those without God's protection. Like the robbers, witches enjoyed causing terror in their own way—setting deadly curses and using magical tricks to manipulate people and circumstances.

On one particular evening, after the hectic market had already closed to shoppers, the men were hungry and exhausted, yet almost too exhausted to care about food.

ANGELS AND WITCHES

One of the abilities of the witches was to become invisible to the human eye. Sometimes, they entered people's homes unseen, wreaking havoc and confusion. That is what two witches planned to do that evening to the young Adventist missionaries.

As the blazing African sun sank low on the horizon, it graced the dusty streets of Kisangani with a golden glow. Two men ducked beneath a loose canopy awning in the empty marketplace and emerged onto the hard-packed red clay street.

"Their house is around the next bend," one said in husky tones.

The other man snickered. "We'll give the *wazungu** quite a show tonight."

As the duo approached the targeted building, they relished the thought of sending the Seventh-day Adventists packing back to America.

Inside the building, Nathan sank into a wooden chair that painfully creaked as he shifted every few minutes. His hand partly obscured his face as he slowly blinked, fighting jet lag and exhaustion. The young American and his friends were visibly weary. "Well, everyone, let's get some sleep," he mumbled. "Tomorrow will be another full day."

Outside, the witches halted in view of the missionary house. A shocking welcome awaited them. A wall of tall and powerful beings surrounded the house; their impenetrable ranks and obvious strength dwarfed the conniving witches.

The two men staggered back in astonishment, then quickly slunk back into the shadows.

Nothing about the night felt strange or different to the young missionary men inside as they retired to rest. They did not detect any special presence in the air or realize that an angel guard surrounded them. Faith in God's calling and His promised presence was enough for them to have peace.

Several days later, one of the witches worked up the courage to approach Pastor Msifiri Mtenzi—a member of the missionary team. While his facial features and accent revealed that the Tanzanian was a foreigner, Mtenzi appeared more approachable because of his darker coloring.

"The people you are working with: Who are they? And why are you with them?" one of the wide-eyed witches asked, gesturing with conviction. Before Mtenzi could open his mouth, the man turned to others nearby and continued, "Listen, these people have strong medicine. Be very careful because a great power is on their side." Who were these people so carefully preserved by an angel army? How loved by God they must be!

---

* *Wazungu* is a Congolese term for Europeans, but is used in a broader sense to mean anyone with pale skin.

As Abigail recalled the inspiring story, a loose chicken suddenly clucked, bringing her thoughts back to the present. She listened in the stillness of the night as crickets croaked out a chorus outside of their home's brick walls.

The mission team still recounted the story of angel protection as a reminder that a handful of volunteers in a remote outpost in Central Africa could not be forgotten by God. It inspired her, but the tales of dishonest thieves and criminal robbers also sent a twinge of foreboding to Abigail's heart. *If witches or robbers visited our campus, would they see a heavenly guard?*

Throughout her childhood, Abigail had dreamed of this time in her life. As a young girl, thoughts of danger and challenges seemed exciting in their distant realities. She wanted to accept a position as a missionary in one of the world's most primitive places and make a difference in the world. Sometimes, she even mentioned in her prayers that she would rather die a martyr than by some ordinary means, as this might bring God the most glory. But today, talk of thieves and robbers, witches and darkness, sent ripples of fright into the twenty-two-year-old's heart. Peril was close enough to touch sometimes—such as when a tsetse fly flew through a vehicle's open window or when an immoral bunch of soldiers eyed the fairest ones of the mission team on a trip through the bush. She realized that it is easy to think one is brave when resting securely at home, but it's a different story in the face of ever-present risk and danger. Just as one might assume that they have inner peace in the absence of war, life's uncertainties and challenges put peace to the true test.

What if darkness tries to strike again? The question cut through the stillness of the night like a knife. The faint rhythm of pounding drums from Huit village joined the nearby whine of a mosquito caught in a fold of mosquito netting. *Tonight, it feels peaceful—but so did that night when Keith, Nathan, and Pastor Mtenzi rested as the witches approached. Dear Lord, please instill peace in my heart to face whatever the future holds.*

As if carried by the warm night breeze whispering through the high decorative bricks above, the assurance came: *You are never forgotten and always loved.*

CHAPTER 3

THE ROCK-THROWING BEGGAR

Although her mind was stirring with a barrage of thoughts, Abigail drifted into a dreamless sleep. The next morning, she shuffled to the outdoor kitchen on the front porch, as was her usual custom, and began to visit with Christopher while she whisked together a batch of pancakes. It wasn't long before Nathan Rittenour came into view and leaned against a porch post. He spoke cheerfully. "Let me know when you're ready to do some printing in the container, Abigail," he said, referring to a shipping container where he housed the mission's printing projects.

Abigail nodded as she filled a bottle with fresh water from the outdoor sink. "I'll be ready in just a few minutes."

"OK," the quiet man nodded in return. "I'll have Kayumba set up the generator for you."

"How was it last night over in the schoolyard?" Christopher asked curiously. He reached for his hat and took long strides across the covered porch.

"It was quiet," Nathan replied. "It wasn't so quiet here on campus at one point, though. Our guard, Bernard, caught a stranger trying to sneak in."

The property had no barrier between it and the jungle. In fact, a trail through the woods led directly from the missionary compound to the rowdy village of Huit. Sometimes locals would emerge out of the woods at random and wander across the campus in curiosity.

Ever interested to know details, Abigail spoke up. "Did Bernard recognize the intruder?"

"Not in the darkness. It was probably someone hoping to steal something."

The three parted ways—Christopher to the Fuso truck, Nathan to the office in search of Keith, and Abigail to the Rittenour home. Upon venturing into the familiar clearing, Abigail found Starla and young Daniel at work in the family's garden.

"Good morning!" Starla pulled her thick black hair into a ponytail and then reached for her young son's hand. "Nathan and I want to offer you a plot in our garden for growing veggies."

"Thank you." Abigail's response was songlike. "I have some seedlings started that I would love to plant. I'm working in the container this morning but can work on the garden when the temperature cools off this evening."

The sun had already begun to heat the air like a sauna. The whitewashed Rittenour home rested snugly against the drab shipping container. Abigail reached for its door handle just as Kayumba brought the generator up to the container entrance. She thanked him profusely. Strong as he was, he huffed as he wrestled with the important piece that provided the power to run the printer, charge the laptop computer on the desk strewn with papers, and keep the air conditioner spewing breezes of luxuriously cold air.

Of course, the air conditioning was not for anyone's personal comfort; the printer required it. Without the cool air in the heat of the tropical weather, the printed ink would turn to powder on the page. In the past, Nathan found that he could easily wipe words away with his hand—a horrifying discovery after he had spent hours formatting documents for printing. Air conditioning made all the difference.

The minutes passed as Abigail worked under the dim light from a bulb hanging precariously from the ceiling. As the young woman folded and stapled a stack of booklets on the plywood countertop, the printer spat out pages nearby. Every so often, her eyes recognized a foreign word in French, Swahili, or Lingala, the Bantu language. "These are my little messengers," she hummed. "They will speak when my voice is silent. They will go places I cannot." She wondered how far God would carry the little books across Congo.

When lunchtime approached, Abigail met Christopher back home on their porch. "I left the printer going back in the container, so I can't stay long," she explained, peering into a pot of boiled beans.

"That's OK," her young husband replied as he sank into a chair. "I have things to do too. I'm organizing a bunch of tools in the depot. Are the beans ready?"

"I sure hope so. I boiled them for hours yesterday." She quickly spooned a heaping serving onto his plate. "Let's hope that they are thoroughly cooked."

Chris sniffed the steaming portion on his plate. "The beans look fine to me," he assured her, shrugging slightly.

As the couple ate, they watched a solitary figure walk from the gravel drive to one of the two small huts nearby. The one-room thatched houses were originally built for student missionaries, but since they had remained empty for a time, Keith Mosier, always generous, was happy to offer them as a living space for several families who worked on campus. As much as Abigail enjoyed privacy in her yard, she appreciated the presence of the families nearby. Community offered safety in Congo. Those isolated were more likely to be targeted for crime.

Joel joined his family on the hard-packed earth beside their dwelling. Joel's wife and a female friend sat under a homemade canopy covered with grass for shade and leisurely swung their legs every so often as they talked. Several children lingered nearby and babbled as they traced circles in the dust with a stick.

"He looks like a kind and cheerful fellow," Abigail said softly, referring to the campus employee. "Isn't his wife one of the three women who responded to your call for baptism some months ago?"

Christopher nodded, a happy light flickering in his eyes. "Yes. I remember that day in the chapel when I first preached, and Keith translated. Keith tells me that the three who responded are studying for baptism currently. Pastor Mtenzi says that he will arrange for me to preach an evangelistic series in Kisangani in a few months."

"Chris," Abigail changed the topic of conversation as she continued to gaze in the direction of Joel's hut. "Do they have food for lunch?"

He glanced over as his wife continued. "The other day, Tammy told me that near the end of the month, many locals go without lunch because funds are tight, and they can't afford beans and rice anymore."

"We *are* nearing the month of September," he said thoughtfully. "Shall we give them the rest of our lunch?"

Abigail jumped up from her chair. "Yes. The beans and rice won't last long without refrigeration anyway, and you know how I dislike wasting food."

"Do you want to invite them to share our lunch?"

"Oh, no, please take it over to them." Abigail quickly averted her gaze. "I feel shy and worried that they will talk fast in Swahili, and I'll be expected to reply but won't understand. It's the story of my life these days."

It was the story of both of their lives in Congo. After a minute of banter over who would carry the food over, Christopher conceded. As he approached the hut with several pans in his hands, Joel and the other adults watched silently.

"A gift," Chris said in Swahili, motioning at the pots.

A flash of realization crossed Joel's face. "Thank you," he said in English, then Swahili, "*Asante*," and then in the country's official language of French, "*Merci*."

The children scampered across the small yard to join the adults around the food, and soon the small group was eating eagerly.

"Oh, Chris, they are hungry," Abigail wrung her hands and paced the cement porch. "Seeing this makes me wish that I hadn't eaten a second serving; it would have left more for them." Joel and his family appreciated the simple gift of the meal. However, not all in Kisangani who appeared in need were happy for food.

Several days later, the Mosiers organized a trip to the city for supplies. The Mosier family led the way in Keith's dusty box cruiser, and Chris followed on a motorbike with Abigail, who held on for dear life over the large dips and around turns in the dirt road.

While Kisangani was heavily populated, the young couple wouldn't have imagined that the city was home to over one million. Rows of tall buildings with chipped paint gave way to an endless array of dirt-colored homes. As their small caravan wound its way through the streets, the Dumans admired the once-glorious colonial city bordered by the mighty Congo River and surrounded by jungle.

Prior to 1965, while under European influence, Kisangani (then Stanley-ville) was a thriving hub of activity where many Rolls-Royce motor cars dotted parking areas shaded by tall palm trees. Hollywood notables visited for rest and relaxation, and a movie featuring actor Audrey Hepburn was filmed here.

What a toll war and violence take on a place, Abigail thought as she watched the Congo River's water glimmer in the afternoon sunlight. A few roughly carved dugout canoes dotted the winding shoreline where speedboats once raced. The dusty streets were now flooded with motorcycles and bicycles, the occasional truck filled with sacks and barrels (sometimes topped with a hapless goat or squealing pig), and policemen searching to discern or fabricate traffic violations. Blocky, colonial-style buildings were faded and peeling, covered with advertisements for Vodacom (a cell phone company) and various brands of motorcycles. Makeshift wooden shacks lined the way with tables of stacked canned goods, meager piles of fresh vegetables gleaned from gardens in the jungle, and cell-phone-minute scratch cards. Years of war left telltale signs in the few charred building storefronts peppered with bullet holes.

Another turn in the winding dirt road revealed a charcoal-colored truck—reduced to a twisted metal frame. Everything that could catch fire inside the vehicle had burned, leaving an empty shell behind.

Christopher slowly guided his motorcycle around the desolate scene as a splash of mud sent a spray up the leg of his jeans.

In the recesses of her mind, Abigail suspected the likely cause of the burned truck. The driver had probably hit someone on the road—not a surprising event, considering the conglomerate of people on the street and disorganized hubbub of drivers combined with few traffic signals and signs. Maybe the unfortunate person had been injured or even died. But someone had gotten angry. At least one set of hands doused the offending vehicle with gasoline. Had the driver escaped the scene alive? It was difficult to say. Maybe Kayumba, who seemed to have connections to news in town, would know.

THE ROCK-THROWING BEGGAR

If any of the missionaries from campus were to accidentally hit someone while on the road, vengeance would be similar and swift. As the small troupe passed through modern-day Kisangani, the missionaries preferred to dwell on more pleasant themes. The Dumans never mentioned the practice of burning vehicles to family and friends back home; it would only create worry over something that it was impossible to do anything about.

"I think of the possibility that we could be involved in an accident every time we drive to town," Starla admitted to Abigail on a previous trip, as they sat in the back seat of the box cruiser while Nathan and Chris ran errands. "All we can do is pray and realize that we are in God's hands."

As the burned truck was left behind, Christopher and Abigail pulled into an unfamiliar section of Kisangani where the streets were cobblestone. Vehicles and motorbikes were less numerous, but locals were not.

"*Wazungu!*" Their entry was heralded with shouts.

Keith led the way to a modest bread shop. All four little Mosier passengers disembarked loudly and then skipped exuberantly across the cobblestones. Tammy and Keith kept close tabs on the blond munchkins as they crossed the road.

The Dumans slowed to a crawl and parked behind the Mosiers' vehicle. Christopher swung a long leg off of the bike and slowly stretched while Abigail removed her motorcycle helmet. She appreciated the privacy from gawking onlookers provided by the face shield.

Almost instantly, a beggar scurried over to the box cruiser. The short young lady was dressed in a flamingo-pink evening gown, and her round face was wreathed in a smile. Unlike many Congolese women in Kisangani, her hair was trimmed very close to her head. Her matching earrings danced, and her eyes glittered as she turned to watch the missionary group enter the bread shop.

Unlike the shopping booths of the hectic outdoor market, the bread shop seemed organized: the baker had placed a variety of loaves behind clear partitions with clearly marked signs to designate each type. The semblance of organization was noteworthy to Abigail as she wandered across the wooden floor and scanned the bakery items. Although gluten and wheat intolerances prevented her from tasting such items in Congo, she didn't feel deprived. She had become used to going without fluffy white pastries and wheat bread.

Tammy pointed to various items and consulted with Keith for a few minutes. Then, with her bags of bread finally in hand, she turned to whisper in Abigail's ear.

"A word of warning about the beggar waiting outside: She's the one I've told you about before."

Abigail's mind raced back to the account she had heard. At one point, a sympathetic foreign visitor had noticed the short beggar woman and wanted to give her a new opportunity to live a fulfilling life. This person donated money to the mission, and the Mosiers dutifully passed the donated funds along to the beggar in increments. But when the money in the fund ran out, they were faced with a problem: the beggar expected a steady stream of money each month. Rumor had it that she squandered her francs on unwholesome and scandalous living—*not* on education or bettering herself. She grew angry when she did not receive the funds, as she had before. How could the mission responsibly help this woman?

Tammy's voice broke into Abigail's recollections. "OK, when we all get in the car, I will hand her a banana or some bread, and then we will need to leave immediately. She often gets upset when we won't give her money and has thrown rocks at us before. No car windows have been broken yet, but I'd rather not risk it, especially having the kids in the car with us today."

Abigail nodded. As she stood on the bread shop step, her gaze lifted to the evening sky. The sun had begun to sink behind the buildings of Kisangani. Another thought crossed her mind, and she quickly turned to Tammy. "It's growing late in the evening, and Chris and I have the motorcycle to drive back on the road to campus. What about thieves?"

Tammy slowly shrugged. "It should be fine if you stick close to our vehicle." There wasn't any good alternate option.

Abigail watched restlessly as her group crossed the street. If they left before the others, would Chris be familiar enough with the city to make it home? Christopher sensed her urgency as she warned him about the stone-throwing beggar and the gathering shadows. He gripped the handlebars and glanced back at Keith. The missionary father settled Anna into the back seat with the beaming beggar close behind, looking both pleased and expectant.

Keith diplomatically smiled at the beggar woman as he carefully shut his vehicle door and slid into the driver's seat. She leaned up against the box cruiser and extended both of her hands.

The missionary nodded his head ever so slightly as he spoke in Swahili. His tone was gracious as he placed several bananas and a loaf of bread in her outstretched palms.

His gaze turned, signaling Chris: *Go!*

Chris didn't waste a second. With a rumble, he pulled the Yamaha motorcycle out into the street.

Suddenly, they were alone—two *wazungu* on a motorcycle—driving through the streets of Kisangani. "Are you sure you know the way back?" Abigail called out over the noise of passing motorbikes.

"I think so," came the reply.

The sun sank lower on the horizon. Their path brought them by the riverside, where mud and mud-colored businesses dotted the shoreline. For a few moments, Abigail could see the rapids—a section of foaming water near the mouth of the Chopo River where locals used nets to catch fish from elevated platforms.

For several minutes, the two Americans were surrounded by other motorists on motorbikes, making it impossible to avoid the many potholes in the road. A policeman watched from a nearby snack stand but made no effort to stop or direct traffic.

Abigail relaxed behind Christopher on the motorbike when they reached the outskirts of town. This was familiar territory, and a police stop was unlikely. She figured that the box cruiser was several minutes behind them.

"I'm going to drive a little faster," he called back to her as they approached the winding jungle road to campus.

"OK," Abigail replied as she readjusted her helmet.

They neared the car wash pond—a soupy spot on the left side of the road where half-naked men covered motorcycles in mountains of soap bubbles. The work-day being over now, locals loitered and settled onto the clumpy grass nearby with jugs in their hands.

"I can smell the alcohol," Chris breathed.

Several yards ahead of them, a motorcycle with two riders was traveling in the same direction. Christopher surged ahead of the motorcycle—but not before recognizing the driver.

It was Kayumba. "Kristoff!" he called out with an expression of laughter and amazement written across his face. He had recognized the pair instantly.

The road had not yet become desolate. Several motorcyclists bumped over the large dips in the road to Kisangani, some carrying loads of cassava and plantains, others, charcoal and wooden branches.

Bernard was assigned to guard the campus for the first watch that evening. Aware that the missionaries had not yet returned, he left the entry gate open. Christopher and Abigail coasted onto the campus property with a smile of relief as they approached their grassy yard.

Dusk had settled over the circle of palms and nearby brick homes when, a few minutes later, Kayumba and his friend rumbled past on the campus drive. By the time the box cruiser full of Mosiers arrived, night had come. They had escaped the beggar before any rocks were thrown, and no one had been stopped by thieves.

"Thank You, Lord, for watching over us." Christopher paused before securing the motorcycle on Keith's caged porch for the night.

"What would you do if a man with a machete blocked our way on the road?" Abigail asked out of curiosity, coaxing her helmet off with a few tugs.

"I think that I would try to quickly drive past him. He would move out of the way if I charged on ahead."

Abigail shrugged. "I hope we never find out."

Back at their house, she heaved a pot of potatoes for soup up onto the small gas stove as she thought about the beggar by the bread shop. The woman in the evening gown and flashing jewelry stood in sharp contrast to Joel's family with their humble clothes and simple lifestyle. She thought it curious that Joel's family might have less than the beggar woman, but they were thankful for their blessings, and she wasn't.

Abigail was learning lessons in the classroom of missionary endeavors. Decisions aren't always cut-and-dried, and heavenly wisdom is needed at every turn.

Her heart was content, knowing that her taken-for-granted blessing of beans and rice was shared with those in need. "This is why we're here: to serve God by serving others," she confided in Christopher. "Some people will be grateful—like Joel and his family—while others will not be so nice—like the rock-throwing beggar. But every effort to show kindness and love is worth it."

"It is." Christopher nodded, then gazed across the dark yard to the light of a cooking fire by Joel's hut. While it was impossible to meet the needs of the whole world, at least they could rest assured that no one in their corner was going hungry tonight.

CHAPTER 4

WELL-DRILLING REVELATIONS

Another day of well drilling in the schoolyard dawned. The sky was clear, and the team of men worked in good spirits.

"No motorcycle accidents have happened today so far," Chris grinned as he joined Abigail for lunch again on the cement porch. "And Nathan thinks that we should be finished with the well by this evening."

"I'd love to see your progress later," Abigail hinted.

"I'll try to take you out on the motorcycle," he promised.

As the afternoon hours passed, Abigail busied herself around the house. She dumped a basket full of dirty laundry into a faded plastic tub, filled the tub with water from an outdoor spigot, then stomped on the laundry with her bare feet. Although Abigail recognized that it was an unconventional process, it did work well to remove much of the mud from Christopher's jeans. *As tempted as I am to hire a helper to wash these, I just don't feel right about it*, she thought. Tammy and Starla hired helpers to wash their clothes and had suggested that Abigail do the same.

Finally hanging the laundry out to dry, Abigail wondered when Christopher would stop by to pick her up. "Maybe he's been too busy," she mused aloud. After reaching for a floppy sun hat, Abigail locked the wooden door to the house and tossed the key into her pocket, setting off on the gravel road to the Mosiers' home.

"The Mosier home is such a warm, welcoming place," she said to herself on the way. "Even the house itself looks friendly to me." Several weeks earlier, Abigail and Christopher had said goodbye to Keith and Tammy after an evening of popcorn, guava smoothies, and family worship on the living room rug. The young couple circled around the house to reach the gravel road but paused for a moment with flashlights in hand. A warm glow exuded from each window as the sound of children's voices traveled on the breeze.

Keith didn't realize that Christopher and Abigail still stood in the yard. Even though it was time for his family to go to sleep, the missionary was ready to welcome any who might need him. "*Karibu* [Welcome]!" he called pleasantly.

"It's just us, Keith," Abigail had called back. "Have a good night!"

That must be why the Mosier home feels so friendly. Abigail mused on her sunny walk to the Mosiers' this day. *The people in it are warm and loving.*

Just then, Alvina came into view around the bend in the road. She walked in her usual fashion—brisk and purposeful. She was a tall, thin woman with deep-set eyes and softly curled hair around her face.

"Abigail, would you like to walk with me to the school? Starla hasn't heard an update from Nathan and sent me out to check on him."

Abigail didn't need a second invitation and quickly changed direction to fall into step with her older neighbor. "Would you have guessed that so many of your children would grow up to be missionaries?" Abigail asked as they passed through the mission gate.

"Actually, it didn't surprise me," came the reply.

"Really?"

"They all wanted to be missionaries when they grew up," she explained softly. "Even the two younger ones."

"The two youngest are in the States now, aren't they?"

"Yes," she straightened her thin shoulders as she rounded a bend in the long mission driveway. "Several years ago, they actually came to Kisangani and helped us with different mission projects. They worked side-by-side with their siblings, Nathan and Tammy. I honestly think they really enjoyed it here."

Abigail sensed there had been a change. "But what happened?"

Alvina sighed. "They left Congo with health issues that were not easily treatable in the United States. The doctors there aren't as familiar with the tropical diseases we have here, and finding a diagnosis can take a long time. Sadly, Peter's lungs have never been the same since he visited here. I think the complications left both of the younger boys feeling discouraged because they had hoped that God would protect them from the diseases here."

For a few minutes, the crunching of Alvina's sneakers over the light gravel was all that broke the silence.

"God doesn't always protect us from pain, but He promises to be with us through it," Abigail said. "Before I first came to Congo, I worried very much that I would contract malaria and be affected by it for the rest of my life."

"You did get malaria, didn't you—before I joined Keith and Tammy here on campus?" Alvina asked. "I heard that you were pretty sick."

"Yes," the younger woman nodded. "During my first few months in Congo, I had fallen ill repeatedly, and then I was bitten by the fateful mosquito. I remember feeling so weak I could barely dress myself or walk. Those days are like a blur to me. But I do remember telling God that I still praised Him—even in the midst of my trial."

"It's easier said than done," Alvina said wisely. "I try to keep a similar habit of praising Him in all things. My children and I have seen some discouraging times as a family . . ." her voice trailed off. After a thoughtful moment, she continued, "But we've had many opportunities to build our faith and trust in God's care and power."

Alvina was not afraid to be vulnerable as she unburdened her heart. She loved her children in the mission field and made the most of life in Congo, but it was not a typical grandparent's retirement destination and probably not Alvina's. If her marriage hadn't heartbreakingly ended in the United States, Abigail wondered how life might look different for the sweet woman.

"I pray that even if my husband and I never get back together again, he will surrender to God. All of this pain I've felt would be worth it if he is brought back to Christ," she affirmed.

Alvina's quiet faith proved a continual inspiration. Abigail often spotted her in the mornings as Alvina walked down the campus road with a notebook spread open in her arms. Even Mamma Rebecca, hoeing in her pineapple garden on early mornings, must have understood that the soft-spoken American woman was deep in prayer. At a time of life when most Americans would have been thinking about retirement and living out the rest of their years comfortably, Alvina spent her days looking after two sets of grandchildren and supporting her son and daughter with their work in Congo. Gathering lemongrass and brewing garlic tea to fend off amoebas, she labored in love without a complaint.

The two women picked their way through a trail of clay muck streaming from the mound where the small rig moaned and clanged. The men hardly looked up from their work as the ladies approached.

"How's it going?" Abigail called up to Christopher on his perch.

He shook his head slightly, sweat standing out on his forehead. He motioned toward his water bottle under Kayumba's baby palm tree nearby, and she quickly passed it up to him, still looking inquiringly.

"We're running into trouble," Nathan explained hastily from his position on the ground. "Drilling has been exceptionally slow. We drew up some of the piping earlier and realized that the water we are using for the drilling process is corroding the metal on the drilling mechanism. Replacing the part should make the process go faster, but now we've lost a pipe down there. I thought we would have this well finished by now, but instead, we are trying to keep the hole from collapsing."

Kayumba and Joel looked very serious and were utterly soaked. Alvina and Abigail joined the circle of workers in the mud as all removed their hats and bowed their heads. "Lord, please bless our efforts and help us find a solution to our problem," Nathan prayed. "See that Your name is glorified through what we do here."

When she returned to the house, Abigail fingered the stiff, sun-dried laundry on her clothesline. She sensed that it would be a lonely evening. Abigail carried the handwashed clothes inside for the night. Once inside, she took a woven sorting basket and began to pick through several cups of beans. Many were shriveled and riddled with holes from tiny bugs.

During her first few months in Congo, Abigail had wondered why some of her cooked beans tasted sour.

"Did you check for holes in the beans?" Tammy had asked matter-of-factly. "You're probably tasting the bug inside."

Enlightened by this new revelation, Abigail ruthlessly inspected bean after bean, tossing out all that floated to the top of the water in the pan (a telltale sign that a bug had taken up residence and created an air pocket inside).

Abigail thought about her afternoon conversation with Alvina. Life seemed so fragile and full of unavoidable risk, whether one lived in the United States or abroad. Reaching for her journal and a pen, she began to write. "I will be very honest. I want to focus on God's grace along my life's journey. In every trial and trouble, I want to give Him praise—as I did when I came down with malaria. But I continue to struggle with some fears that I dare not share with even my parents and siblings back home for fear that they would worry too much."

For a few moments, she continued to write, reflecting on the recent visit to Kisangani.

Every trip I take into town is a risk. The locals here are prone to swift vengeance before asking questions. Vehicles and their occupants are burned when accidents happen on the road—and one of our Congolese workers was beaten for accidentally sliding into a house on his motorcycle during the rainy season. When people do survive accidents, medical care is limited and questionable. Several of the missionaries and I stopped at a clinic once and learned that the medical workers were drawing patients' blood without ever changing needles. (No wonder diseases spread so quickly!) Also, robbers are a constant concern in this area. Stories of their cruelty and frequent stops in the area (including at nearby Huit village) give me shivers. But I know that God is with us and that He unquestionably led us here.

Abigail took a deep breath as she wrote, trying to accept that her life and experiences were very much outside of her control. "And all I can do is trust my life to His hands."

WELL-DRILLING REVELATIONS

Abigail felt relieved as she finished writing down her thoughts. "True peace only comes through resting in the Lord's will. Do I value perceived convenience and safety more than this peace?"

As dusk settled over the campus, Abigail geared up for a trip among the malaria-causing mosquitoes by donning a pair of leggings, lacing up her boots, and dousing herself in a cloud of bug spray. As she locked the front door behind her and set off down the road again, she guessed that Starla would have news about the well-drilling effort.

Light gleamed from the Rittenour home. Abigail softly knocked on the door, and Alvina ushered her inside. Starla sat on the living room couch with golden-haired Daniel on her lap, reading the last few sentences of a Bible story. She glanced up briefly with a smile in her dark eyes.

"Let me put him down for bed, and then let's drive down to the schoolyard," she suggested, with Daniel now perched on her hip. The little guy yawned and rubbed his eyes with chubby fists. "You'll stay here in case he wakes up, won't you, Alvina?"

"Yes," her mother-in-law returned. "I do have a phone call to make, so I'll be in the next room. But I will listen for Daniel if he cries."

"We won't be gone long," Starla assured her.

Alvina paused with her hand on the door to the next room. "Peter messaged me earlier today and said that he wanted me to call him," she explained.

"I hope he is doing well," Starla said of her brother-in-law. She grabbed a flashlight from a nearby shelf and turned to Abigail. "Are you ready?"

They trekked over to the mission vehicle, and Starla turned the key in the ignition. Bright beams from the headlights lit up the dense darkness before them. "Let's see, the brake usually works," Starla said with a good deal of pluck as she tested it. "OK, there. It's working. First, let's go to the well in the center of campus and fill up water jugs for the men. I'm sure that they're out of drinking water by now."

The box cruiser slowly bumped over the gravel road. Several hired workers with machetes had cut the grass by hand a week earlier, which made the going easier as the two women lurched through the greenery. When they stepped out of the cruiser and approached the pump in the illumination of the bright car beams, Abigail slowly realized that they were being watched. From multiple homes surrounding the green, Congolese workers peered from their windows at the peculiar spectacle of these two foreign women struggling to pump water at night.

"We can do this, Abby," Starla breathed as she grasped the pump handle. The water came in cold gushes as Abigail held up a jug to catch the stream.

A lone figure in checkered pajama pants and an old T-shirt emerged from the shadows: it was Mamma Rebecca's husband, who often served as one of the campus guards but must have been off-duty at the moment. "I will help you," he managed to say in staccato-like English.

"Thank you," Starla stepped aside as the strong man took over at the pump. Knowing few Swahili words, she said nothing more but looked up at him gratefully before he slipped away again. The jugs were full to the brim now.

"We must have piqued some curiosity," Abigail giggled to Starla as they hopped up into the vehicle. "I see people peering from their windows all around the green."

Just a few minutes later, they were almost to the drilling site. The tall grasses on each side of the road and the frequent dips made Abigail imagine that she was on a safari. "Aren't you glad we don't have to worry about lions here?" she quipped.

Finally, they pulled into the schoolyard and walked into the dim light of the well rig and a circle of exhausted men.

"We've made a breakthrough," Nathan announced, having regained his exuberance in spite of being completely soaked in a mixture of mud, water, and bentonite. To the newcomers, it looked as if he had taken a dive into the big piles of slime that surrounded the machine.

Starla's face was aglow in the light of the vehicle's headlights. She listened as Nathan talked and nodded to affirm her comprehension.

"We should be finished in a few minutes—thanks for the water," he said as he took a bottle from his wife. "We're starved. Could you have some banana smoothies waiting for us at the house?"

For hours, the men had stood under the searing African sun, sloshing through mud and chugging down water. They brainstormed and prayed above the noise of the rig and nearby generator as supper time had come and gone.

Christopher's hair was wet; his face was peppered with muddy clay. He barely paused to take a drink from the jug of water Abigail handed up to him. She recognized the determined set of his jaw and knew that he would see the project through if it took him all night. He nodded to Kayumba, who steadied a pipe in his hands and flashed a smile in the shadows. Their goal was within reach.

The two women returned to the Rittenour house again, and Starla exchanged places with Alvina to watch over Daniel. Alvina and Abigail walked to the Mosiers' to use their blender for the men's smoothies. Theirs was the only house on campus with a Vitamix, a refrigerator, and a chest freezer: all used by multiple families. Keith and Tammy Mosier were generous and always willing to share the items.

"Watch out for the army ants," Abigail warned Alvina, keeping her flashlight pointed at the ground. "I saw a trail of them crossing the path earlier today."

WELL-DRILLING REVELATIONS

The ants were still there. They never seemed to cease their constant travels, even at night. Everyone on campus—from wise Pastor Mtenzi down to little Talitha Mosier—was acquainted with the pain inflicted by their strong jaws. Abigail personally detested the ants. They were tiny but dangerous for the feeble Congolese or helpless infants. They traveled through dwellings and sheds, ferociously consuming whatever was alive and lying in their path.

Later that evening, with banana smoothies in hand, the men recounted the day's events. "We were praying for a solution," Nathan began, "when I saw that the water that we were using to drill down was actually corroding the metal. This small part was the problem. Chris, do you have the piece?"

The blond twenty-six-year-old sank into the couch before handing it over. Nathan inspected the round tube in his calloused hands. "This was the last well I had intended to use this part on."

"And what about the fallen pipe?" Alvina inquired.

"The pipe is out, and the well is a keeper."

A spirit of joy and thankfulness settled around the room. The conversation changed from events close by in Congo to loved ones far away in the States.

"I talked with Peter this evening," Alvina announced quietly. "He is personally struggling right now and seems unsure of his life purpose. Will each of you keep him in prayer?" Her dark eyes traveled around the room searchingly. The mother's heart obviously yearned for her son's salvation. "Can we pray right now?" she persisted.

Together, the two couples knelt on the cement floor along with loving Alvina and sent petitions heavenward.

In her growing-up years, Abigail had often heard prayers on behalf of the missionaries and their struggles abroad. She always felt that God's messengers in the foreign field needed much prayer. But on this night, as she knelt on the cement floor, she realized that missionaries pray just as earnestly for the loved ones they leave back home. The cement felt like holy ground as heartfelt words of prayer ascended.

A question suddenly pressed on her heart: Could it be that they were spiritually safer in Congo than they would be in the United States? *We may live in a country scarred by war and touched by poverty. Thieves may tramp our roads through the night. The presence of disease and darkness surrounds us. But we have direction here, a purpose that so many people don't have. We know that heaven is our home, and we trust ourselves to the mighty hand of God to protect and guide us.*

A sense of peace settled upon the room as all returned to their chairs. The men were tired but happy. Little Daniel slept quietly in the nearby bedroom as the crickets chirped outside on the lawn. A gentle assurance rested in each heart that God had heard and that He would send his angels to answer their prayers.

With a contented sigh, Keith reached for his guitar. "I'd like to sing a song together before you leave." A happy light shone in his eyes as he began.

"The golden morning is fast approaching;
Jesus soon will come
To take His faithful and happy children
To their promised home.
O, we see the gleams of the golden morning
Piercing through this night of gloom!
Oh, we see the gleams of the golden morning
That will burst the tomb."[1]

After the music faded away, a peaceful silence pervaded the living room until Keith spoke. "I think of this song as the theme song of our mission here," he said as he ran his hand across the smooth guitar finish. "We see gleams of light piercing the darkness of this world. Oh, what a happy day it will be when Jesus comes for us."

"Amen," came Alvina's quiet voice from the corner of the room.

As Christopher and Abigail walked home to their brick house under a brilliant canopy of stars, Abigail attempted to organize her thoughts more clearly.

"You know that the thought of danger here frightens me sometimes," she started, reaching for his hand in the darkness. "But I realize that to rest in the center of God's will is to dwell in the safest place of all."

He gave her hand a squeeze. "That's right."

"Isn't it amazing to know that God wants us here, right here in Congo, right now, doing this work?" she breathed.

"Yes, it is," he said slowly. "It's a wonderful feeling."

She paused, returning to her earlier thoughts. "We are actually in a safe place. Those who are in far greater danger are people who have not given Christ their all—people who have not surrendered for one reason or another."

Chris turned to her in the darkness. "True safety is found in walking with God, even if it is in a dangerous place, Abigail."

---

1. S. J. Graham, "Gleams of the Golden Morning" (1900).

CHAPTER 5

SABBATH PEACE

The workweek drew to a close. Abigail labored with renewed energy in the printing container, tended to her garden under Starla's botanical guidance, and felt a new assurance that she rested in the Lord's will. The well at the schoolhouse required only a few finishing steps to be functional, and Sabbath promised new blessings.

Starla stood outside her whitewashed house bright and early on Sabbath morning. "Come, Daniel, it's time to get in the car and go to church." She beckoned for her little boy.

"Safe, safe!" Daniel toddled to her waiting arms.

"Yes," she agreed as she settled him on her hip. "You are safe."

Christopher and Abigail heard the brief exchange as they ambled up to the house to carpool with the Rittenours.

"Ever since Daniel was nearly hit by someone on a motorcycle in our yard, Nathan and I have been encouraging him to be a little more cautious," Starla explained as Nathan tossed a diaper bag into the vehicle.

The mission's box cruiser bumped down the mission driveway, full of familiar passengers. Nathan clutched the vibrating steering wheel as Alvina shared the passenger's seat with the Mosier family's helper, Mamma Nikke. In the open bench seats in the rear, Starla held little Daniel with one hand and her diaper bag with the other.

"How has Daniel's breathing been?" Alvina asked from the front.

"It is fine now, but we had another difficult night last night because of his coughing and breathing issues," Starla replied. "I had to use the inhaler we brought him from the States."

Nathan slowed the vehicle to a stop by a brick home near the office. "We're stopping to pick up Kayumba and his family," he explained.

Starla glanced up from running her fingers through Daniel's blond hair. "Do we have enough room?"

As if in answer, Kayumba unlatched the back of the box cruiser and lifted his children inside, one by one. They were dressed in the best clothes that they could find at the market—largely unwanted thrift store castoffs from other countries and sold in bulk to humble Congolese business owners. Kayumba's wife, Esther, smoothed the folds of her printed polyester skirt before she reached for their baby in Kayumba's arms.

"This road has dried considerably since our last downpour," Nathan observed as he maneuvered the vehicle around a large pothole.

The property to the left of the road was owned by a Catholic organization. The fields were sprawling and pleasant, lined with sturdy trees and dotted with brown cows. A few months earlier—when one section in the road became a virtual pond of mud—locals decided to bypass the road by cutting through the field.

"It appears that the Catholics are fixing it," Alvina mumbled from the front seat. Two Congolese men were carefully fixing the breaks with barbed wire.

"The locals will only tear it down again when they see the need," Starla remarked with a hint of humor.

As the vehicle pulled into a small clearing beside a Seventh-day Adventist church in Kisangani, adults and children stormed the vehicle with waves and smiles. As soon as the back door opened, a little figure planted herself at its opening. Nathan set Daniel down on the car bumper for a moment and reached for his Bible, but he didn't act quickly enough.

The bold little girl reached for Daniel with her arms outstretched. She hoisted him onto her hip in older-sibling fashion. Without hesitation, she switched him over to her back and set off in the direction of the church. A crowd of excited children surrounded her with admiring looks as she paraded the American toddler riding piggyback.

"Oh no!" Starla gasped. "Nathan!" After taking a few quick strides, Nathan pulled his son off the little girl.

Abigail noticed that the young girl didn't act disappointed. She turned and fearlessly gazed at the Americans, locked eyes with Abigail, and then courageously reached for her hand. The beginning of a familiar hymn wafted on the breeze as the two walked together to the church entrance, and then the little girl disappeared into the crowd.

"What is it about this girl that is so striking?" Abigail wondered. Nothing about the seven- or eight-year-old looked much different from any average Congolese girl—the short-ruffled skirt, the red T-shirt, and the dark hair pulled sharply away from her oval face. But something about her fearless gaze and confident demeanor stood out to Abigail.

The missionaries paused for a moment as church elders scrambled to find their best chairs for their important guests.

"Are you ready to speak?" Nathan whispered to Abigail from a blue plastic lawn chair nearby. "Our translator is here and ready."

She nodded and followed Christopher to the head of the congregation. All eyes fell on the couple as they opened their Bibles, and Abigail spoke about reconciliation.

"If Kristoff and I had an argument," she gestured to her husband and used the French version of his name, "and instead of coming up with a solution, we talked to everyone else about the issue, would we have a good marriage?"

A knowing snicker erupted from the ladies in the audience. Even serious Mamma Nikke smiled.

"Back in America, Kristoff and I have a home with a neighbor nearby. We have a dog that loves to wander into the neighbor's yard and steal their things. This is bad," she said, wincing at a few memories. "But worse for us was the fact that our neighbors did not talk to us about the problem. Instead, they talked to Kristoff's mother."

Congolese families were close-knit. Abigail felt certain that they understood when she heard an audible "ooh" sweep through the audience.

"Just as our neighbors should have talked to us about the problem, you in the church family should go to the person who offended you to solve the issue instead of talking about it to everyone else."

Abigail nodded to Christopher, who picked up where she left off. "Love is a choice," he stated as he closed. "Overcome evil with good. Jesus loves us and asks that we love all of His children just as He does."

The Sabbath School portion of the service ended, and Nathan disappeared behind a large red curtain to pray with the elders before the church service began. The missionary man approached the congregation with a sparkle in his eyes and eagerness in his steps.

"Nathan obviously has a message on his mind," Abigail whispered to Christopher on the bench beside her.

"I would like to talk about something important today—about anger and fear versus love," Nathan began simply. "Every adult in this room has probably tried to dodge policemen in town. I have seen police desperately try to stop motorcycles to check their papers, but no one wants to stop. I have seen officers poke a stick between the turning wheels of the motorcycle or try to pull the keys out of the ignition. The policemen get very angry."

The audience nodded knowingly.

Kayumba had tried to dodge an officer in Kisangani just a few days earlier. While traversing a narrow place in the street, he was singled out by an officer who jammed a branch through his tire spokes. Kayumba waited miserably as the man in uniform looked for a reason to write a fine and then gleefully learned that Kayumba worked for the missionaries. "Thieves," Kayumba spat out the word as he received the francs from Nathan to pay the fine.

"Just like the police in town, people will show anger to create fear," Nathan continued. "But this is not God's way. The law of heaven is love. God does not force us to love or to pray—instead, He wants us to give Him our devotion willingly."

Nathan carefully tied his opening illustration with the practical concept of parenting.

"In a different Congolese city lived a mother who often grew angry with her child. One day in a fit of anger, she actually grabbed a stick out of the fire and burned the back of his leg with it. From then on, the child obeyed, but it was only out of fear." The large room grew very silent as the people listened. "When the rest of the children in the area saw what the mother did to her son, they went to the mother's house and burned it down. Now the mother is afraid because of the children's anger. You see, anger and fear only breed more anger and fear."

On more than one occasion, Abigail had observed severe discipline in her own front yard. Joel's wife sometimes yelled and shook their children in anger. It was painful for Abigail's sensitive spirit to observe, and she wished that someone would address the topic of parenting in anger. Today, she felt a rush of relief to hear Nathan speak.

Nathan talked like a convicted man, and his words grew more pointed as he continued. "We do not correct sin with sin." His eyes were searching. "So, what will you be to your children? Will you correct them in love and gentleness so that they can grow to be straight and true in the law of heaven? Or will you teach them anger and fear by your own example? That is the question today."

The service closed with another song. Abigail blinked for a few moments before she recognized it in the guise of Swahili.

> Take the name of Jesus with you,
> Child of sorrow and of woe;
> It will joy and comfort give you,
> Take it, then, wher-e're you go.
> Precious name, O how sweet!
> Hope of earth and joy of heaven.[1]

"We are family," Abigail realized. "As humans, we face the same life struggles." There was no black or white in the room: only brothers and sisters created in God's image.

Nathan quietly rejoined Starla in his faded lawn chair. He reached for Daniel and settled him on his knee, scanning the crowd as the people filed into the churchyard. Before the missionaries exited the building, a circle formed outside on the dusty ground. As each person left the sanctuary, they filed down a line of warm handshakes and singing and then took their place at the end of a long line that circled around the entry. When the song reached a close, everyone in the building had clasped every person's hand.

The mission campus was quiet that afternoon. Christopher and Abigail raided Keith's library at the office before settling down under their mosquito net to read. Abigail paused to think about the little girl with the strong gaze at the church in Kisangani. *She recognized that she was just as valuable a person as we were. That was it! She was not afraid to reach out and touch us.* Abigail hoped that her little friend would never let go of courage. She prayed that no matter what life brought the young girl, she would cling fiercely and faithfully to truth and love.

Before turning out the light that night, Abigail reached for a familiar blue notebook from the makeshift bookcase of boards. "Sometimes, I wonder if the Lord is asking Chris and me to stay here indefinitely or that maybe He wants to know what I am willing to give up for His sake. While my soul pines for my loved ones back home and for the luxuries I enjoyed there, my heart wants to rest in the center of God's will. So, if He asks me to stay here forever, I will." This new surrender felt peaceful, even significant. "Whatever He asks of me, the answer is yes."

---

1. Lillian Baxter, "Take the Name of Jesus With You" (1870).

CHAPTER 6

OVER THE RIVER AND THROUGH THE JUNGLE

H ere comes Nathan." Christopher watched the purposeful figure approach from the gravel drive. The man's average frame was bent in determination as he walked, and his eyes scanned the vegetation at his feet with a serious expression on his face.

Abigail smiled as she scrubbed potatoes by the outdoor sink. "That man is always on a mission."

After approaching the couple on the porch, Nathan gave an absentminded greeting and plunged into relating his well-drilling plans for the future. "I realize that the well is still not complete at the schoolhouse, but I need to make a trip to Isangi to determine the drilling conditions there. I've heard that the people in Isangi desperately need clean water, and the rainy season is almost upon us. When the rains come, it will be too difficult to traverse the road to Isangi." Nathan clamped a calloused hand onto a porch beam nearby. "I'm wondering if you would accompany me, Chris. Kayumba will go with us as well."

Christopher's eyes said yes before the word came from his mouth.

"We may have to spend the night, so we will have to load a few motorcycles with tents and supplies," Nathan added.

Abigail looked up suddenly from the outdoor sink. "May I join you?" She would rather spend the night in the jungle with Christopher than sleep in their campus home alone.

"Certainly," Nathan nodded. But he then warned her that the journey would be ninety-four miles one way, traversing conditions comparable to a motocross off-road race.

"Meet me in the printing container in a few minutes," he called out as he launched off the porch in that direction.

Kayumba and Joel joined the Dumans in the container and watched as Nathan traced a hand-drawn map with his finger. Churches, roads, and waterways were all clearly marked in black and blue permanent markings. "We will go through Kisangani, then cross the Chopo River in a dugout. Our second river crossing will be over the Congo River basin near Isangi. Prepare to leave at six o'clock tomorrow morning."

Abigail rushed through the rest of the afternoon as she processed more books and tracts for sharing and then packed for the trip.

The next morning was brisk, and a thick mist rolled through the surrounding tropical forest. Two motorcycles rolled up to the campus office. Christopher and Abigail were in the lead, and Nathan and Kayumba followed on the second bike. Christopher revved the engine every now and then just to hear the sound. Keith met the small group on the porch, smiling as usual.

"Let me pray with you before you leave," the husband and father said as all heads bowed. "We place our traveling friends in Your hands, Lord," Keith began. "Please bless their efforts, and may the Congolese be reminded that there is a God who loves and cares for them."

As the men exchanged final words, Abigail smiled softly. "In His hands is the safest place to be," she whispered.

"Pastor Mtenzi and I will be keeping you especially in prayer today," Keith called out from the office porch. "Go with God's blessing!"

The murky gray of dawn slowly lifted. Christopher's jaw tensed with excitement as he pulled in behind Kayumba and Nathan on the winding road to Kisangani.

Locals watched curiously when the small group reached the Chopo River landing. Several women shyly smiled as they spread out their wares on tables. Free-range chickens squawked, and tethered goats bleated. Men pushed motorcycles with heavy loads of cassava leaves, baskets, and bananas along the gradual incline to the water's edge. The frothing waves lapped at the shoreline, and naked children dipped in the muddy brown river. Their mothers watched nearby, coating the water with soap bubbles as they washed clothes with their strong brown arms. After selecting a large, smooth-topped rock, the women plunged pants and shirts into the water, slapped them across the stone surface, and then vigorously scrubbed them with a bar of soap. Abigail observed that the Congolese were a very clean people. They bathed often and hand washed clothes with a violence that wore out the very best quality secondhand clothing.

Wooden dugouts, hollowed out from stout tree trunks in the forest, waited at the river's edge to take motorcycles across. The ferry on the opposite side of the river was stationary; it was still too early to begin the slow river crossings.

"I say she's about fifteen years old." A local casually leaned an arm across his motorbike and eyed Abigail, the youngest member of the group.

"No, more like seventeen," another said hopefully. Neither seemed in much of a hurry to cross the Chopo that early morning.

Nathan happened to overhear the conversation at hand while Kayumba haggled for a fair crossing price at the river's edge. "She's married to the man whom she shares the motorcycle with," Nathan called out with the hint of a smile. He nodded to Christopher before the missionary party left the two disappointed men behind.

In the minds of many Congolese men, marrying an American foreigner was a coveted arrangement. Besides being somewhat of a novelty, the common thinking was that all Americans were rich, and they lived in a crazy country akin to the wild west—full of guns and bombs. Yet, the Americans seemed quite harmless when displaced in the Democratic Republic of Congo. On one occasion, a random young stranger even called out an "I love you" to Abigail in the marketplace. His English was limited, but he gave it a try anyway.

Christopher and Kayumba hoisted the two motorcycles into a dugout, and Nathan and Abigail carefully boarded the vessel.

Morning sunlight glimmered over the widening expanse of water between them and the shore. Battling the current, the owners of the canoe pointed it upstream and paddled it expertly. "I once saw a hippo in this river, but I assume that it's since been eaten by locals," Nathan remarked.

"Who would want to eat a hippo?" Abigail mused.

Nathan laughed. "People eat everything here. A lot of the jungle wildlife is scarce because of hunting. Most hunters are limited to mongoose and rats now, although they sometimes find monkeys in the deep jungle."

"But what about the elephants and other wild animals one thinks of when Africa comes to mind?"

"There might be some very deep in the jungle," Nathan said thoughtfully. "The dense forests could hide a lot more than we think."

Once across the river, the four travelers remounted their motorbikes. They had just passed through a small village when some policemen brought them to a halt. The Dumans watched silently as the men in blue uniforms and caps hounded Kayumba over a missing traveler's document—a classic moneymaking tactic.

Although the humidity and temperatures soared, Kayumba did not remove his puffy long-sleeved coat. He reached into the loose brown sack around his neck and retrieved a small stack of French booklets. Something about them seemed very familiar to Abigail as she watched closely. Why, these were the booklets she had printed only a few weeks before!

Kayumba distributed a booklet to each of the policemen. Several of them opened the cover and began slowly flipping through the pages. One policeman who appeared to be the leader turned and gestured with his hand for the group to pass on—he was satisfied with the gift.

The dirt road followed the Chopo River for many miles. Kayumba, Nathan, Christopher, and Abigail passed village after village, where children yelled and scampered after them. At one point, Nathan gestured to a small clearing nearby where there was a fine-looking well.

"He must have drilled that well before we came here," Christopher explained to Abigail as they quickly passed by—but not without noticing that many people were enjoying the well water in the climbing warmth of the day.

By midmorning, the bumps and turns had become very unpleasant to the young couple. When the road finally smoothed out for a stretch, Abigail loosened her grip on Christopher to pray and sing into the confines of her helmet.

The trail led into an area of mature forest, which sheltered the small group from the hot sun. Cool breezes brushed across Abigail's arms. They had reached unfamiliar territory now. They passed through Yangambi—once a thriving community with over 250 homes, an herbarium, and a library. The once-active research hub was nearly a ghost town now, barely maintained by a skeleton crew living in dilapidated buildings surrounded by an immense swath of jungle.

Every so often, through the trees, Abigail glimpsed a faded but upscale Belgian house standing silently. Children dressed in rags watched from overgrown yards where the jungle was creeping in to hide the century-old homes. *I feel like I've walked into scenes from an old movie and not real life*, she marveled.

The winding road grew incredibly rough. At one point, it had been a beautiful travel way paved with cobblestones. Now, great masses of the road material lay in heaps while other areas were missing stones entirely. A cement drainage ditch lined the road to the left, and brick culverts bulged out from the disorganized remnants of a once-beautiful road.

At the end of the Belgian occupation, when Congo reached independence, most of the inhabitants of Yangambi fled. Abigail guessed that since the Belgians left, not many other Americans had seen this place. As they neared the Congo River's edge again, more signs of life appeared. A few sellers lined the streets under makeshift canopies. Behind them stood brick buildings with broken glass and other evidence that this had been a prosperous town years ago.

Chris raised his voice over the hum of the motorcycle. "Keith told me that cholera used to be pretty bad up this way."

By the time they reached the Congo River crossing, Abigail felt dehydrated and walked unsteadily on her feet.

"How in the world can Kayumba still be wearing that thick coat?" she panted as they reached the river's edge.

Christopher merely chuckled as he slowly removed his helmet.

Abigail forgot all about heat and hunger when they met their waiting dugout canoe; it hugged the sprawling roots of an old tree and was already packed with occupants and motorcycles.

"Careful," Christopher warned as he helped his wife onto the boat. It trembled and swayed as she picked her way to an open spot where she could sit. More locals loaded aboard.

We are in God's hands, Abigail reminded herself in an effort to mask her dissatisfaction. She realized that most Congolese could not swim. If the boat capsized into the Congo's mighty depths, the result would be sheer terror. "Not a soul has a life jacket on this boat," she whispered to Christopher in amazement.

"Nope," he replied matter-of-factly.

Not until the boat hit Isangi's sandy shoreline did Abigail breathe a little easier. The sprawling town was unusually quiet as they pulled up to the flat banks. This area was once a site where Arabian traders stopped for ivory and slaves. Unfortunately, these practices did not end when Belgian King Leopold claimed the country as his "free state." In 1888, a Zanzibar-based slave trader established a station in the community, enabling him to capture slaves along the nearby rivers.

A local with a bicycle agreed to lead the missionaries to the nearby Adventist church.

Isangi frequently experiences torrential downpours, storms, and even tornadoes. The winding dirt paths were muddy from recent rains, and Kayumba momentarily lost control of the motorcycle as he followed the bicyclist. His feet jerked from the pedals to the ground as he endeavored to steady the machine. The bike spun in the mud, leaving a deep rut for hapless Christopher to navigate as Kayumba set off again.

European missionaries had visited this area of the Congo in years past. It was rumored that several miles upstream, foreign hands had planted a stand of date palms that were still living. A Catholic church was the most notable building in Isangi—and strikingly ornate. A Protestant presence had also remained through the years.

The small group pulled into a clearing shaded by sturdy mango trees where a simple Seventh-day Adventist church building of earth tones blended in with the setting.

"Kayumba," a warm, strong voice boomed. A smiling young man grasped Kayumba's puffy coat sleeve, and the two immediately broke into discourse.

Nathan mechanically dismounted from the motorbike and dusted the dirt from his pants. The dirt from the past ninety-four miles had been substantially augmented by Kayumba's mud bath episode en route.

The smiling young church planter quickly gathered lawn chairs for his visitors, and little children with protruding bellies flocked at a cautious distance from the semicircle. When the visitors were finally settled under a tree, they shared a lunch of boiled potatoes and spoke with the area's church planter.

"Cholera has devastated this community." The church planter shook his head. "Good water would be a true blessing to our village."

"We passed a well on our way from the river. Is it in use?" Nathan asked.

"Yes, but the well was dug by hand years ago, and there is no sanitary seal. We are thankful it has a cover. Many villages aren't even that lucky. Small animals fall in and decay because there is nothing to prevent it." A little girl confidently approached his chair and climbed into his lap. She snuggled into the crook of his arm and watched Kayumba chew on a loaf of crusty bread.

Nathan nodded. "Chlorine tablets should be used in water that is not clean, but I understand that they can be difficult to obtain." His gaze grew distant and thoughtful, pausing as if there was so much more on his heart for this nation than he could ever say. He blinked and returned to the subject at hand. "What is the ground like here, in terms of well-drilling? Is it rocky?"

The man nodded, cradling his little girl in his arms that bore tattoos partially obscured by his crisp white T-shirt. "Yes, the soil is very rocky—we have a lot of packed red rock here."

Kayumba looked over at the little girl on his friend's lap and handed her a piece of bread and half of his avocado. Accepting the items wordlessly, she watched him with big brown eyes and wound her fingers tightly around her new treasures.

"Thank you for your time," Nathan said as he rose to his feet. "That is the information I needed. My team will try to reach home before dark tonight, so we must be going."

Hope for the future shone in the church planter's eyes as he shook Kayumba's hand again and watched the two motorcycles sputter out of sight.

Kayumba was still wearing his puffy overcoat as the group boarded a less-crowded dugout in the direct sun. Sweat beaded on everyone's brow.

"Bukavu is further upriver." Nathan told Chris.

"The place where I was bitten by the malaria mosquitoes!" Abigail remembered the occasion wryly.

The Congo River stretched a sizable distance from shore to shore. Abigail marveled at its winding shoreline and the multiple islands packed with jungle shrubbery at its center. Peering into the depths, she wondered how deep the water below them was. But she figured that it stayed true to its reputation as one of the deepest rivers in the world with depths of up to 720 feet.

Arriving back at the sprawling roots of the mango tree on the other side, Christopher and Kayumba heaved the two motorcycles from the canoe. Everyone climbed astride, and once again, they wound their way along the Yangambi reserve, enjoying the natural air conditioning that the thick jungle provided.

Kayumba's grip on the motorcycle handlebars tightened until his knuckles were white. His face looked pensive. Time was running out for the group to reach Kisangani by nightfall. He seemed to sense that Nathan would rather stop early to camp than travel the winding road from Kisangani to the campus at night. Maybe his motivation to increase the pace was the thought of sleeping by the road instead of enjoying dinner with Esther and their children. But whatever the case, his hand tightened on the accelerator, and his bike steadily gained speed.

Christopher observed the acceleration with some amusement. Finally, Kayumba was forced to stop before entering an old iron bridge. Nathan and Abigail dismounted, allowing their drivers to maneuver across the wooden planks.

"We are making good time, aren't we, Nathan?" Abigail asked as she crossed the bridge on foot, taking care not to catch her shoe in the wide cracks between the planks.

Nathan laughed. "I think Kayumba overheard that we would be tenting tonight. But yes, at this rate, we will be able to safely traverse the road out to the campus before dusk."

Abigail sighed with relief. She had never spent nine hours on a motorcycle before, and every muscle in her body screamed. The thought of sleeping on her springy Congolese mattress back on campus that night had never seemed so appealing.

Kayumba surged ahead once again as Nathan held on to the luggage rack with both hands. They approached a section of the gravel road where water drainage had made little rivulets as it coursed across from one side to the other. The small front wheel of Kayumba's motorcycle caught in one of them and jerked to the side. As the bike veered sharply to the right, the Congolese lost control. The motorbike with its two riders careened into a ditch about ten feet ahead of the Dumans' motorcycle and nearly disappeared out of sight. The only item left on the road was Kayumba's white hard hat, which had flown fifteen feet in the opposite direction.

Christopher quickly slowed to a stop and leaped from his motorcycle.

A pained expression registered on Kayumba's face as he reached for his knee. He painfully pulled himself out of the grassy ditch to reveal a disheveled Nathan, whose full body weight had landed on the light-framed Congolese in the spill.

Abigail ran to retrieve Kayumba's hard hat, but her legs only seemed to wobble. "Similar to my dreams when I try to run, and I can't seem to," she chuckled. After picking up the muddy hat, she sighed. "So much for head protection!" There were no straps to hold it in place around Kayumba's chin.

"Are you OK?" Christopher asked his friends.

"OK . . ." Kayumba's voice trailed off as if questioning himself. "I think I'm OK."

Without protest, he allowed Nathan to take the handlebars the rest of the way home.

"Kayumba could have easily broken a leg," Chris remarked as they set out again at a slower pace. "That could have ended badly."

Despite the motorcycle accident, they reached campus before sunset, and Kayumba returned to his home and family. Abigail's eyes burned from the road dust as she mechanically followed Christopher and Nathan to the Mosiers' house, where supper was waiting on the long wooden table.

"Our friends are back!" Keith welcomed the weary three warmly.

"I've been spending the afternoon here at the Mosiers," Starla explained to Nathan. She spooned mashed banana into Daniel's mouth and then repositioned herself to give her husband a hug. "I've noticed that Daniel is having a difficult time breathing during his nap times at our house. It worries me. What will we do when his inhaler is used up? There's no replacement for it in Congo."

Nathan placed a hand on her shoulder reassuringly. "We should check the house for mold. Can you tell if he's breathing better here at Keith and Tammy's?"

"Yes," she nodded quickly. "I think I can tell a difference."

After he blessed the meal, Keith quizzed Nathan about the trip. "Do you think that the town of Isangi is a likely candidate for a drilled well?"

"The roads are decent, all things considering," his brother-in-law replied. "I checked the bridges, and I think that they can hold the weight of the small rig. Unfortunately, though, Isangi is home to a lot of red rock, and I'm not sure if the rig we have will be able to handle the intensity of the drilling."

Keith stayed optimistic. "When the large well drilling rig arrives here from the United States, it will be able to handle the bigger jobs."

"Yes," Nathan replied matter-of-factly. "Our Isangi drilling may have to wait for the arrival of the big rig."

"Would anyone like some tea?" Alvina poured a cup for young Caleb Mosier. The four-year-old grasped the mug with both hands and took eager gulps. "It has a lot of fresh garlic and lemongrass, and I think it helps the kids maintain a good immune system," Alvina explained. "It's good for fending off amoebas too."

Abigail didn't feel a great urge to drink it, but she watched Caleb curiously. "I'm amazed that it is such a hit with the kids," she confided in low tones.

"Well, I do put a fair amount of stevia sweetener in it," Alvina responded hastily.

"When Grandpa Barry arrives soon, we should have him try your tea—don't you think, Shiloh?" Tammy sounded mischievous.

"Yes," the precocious young blond replied, wiggling in her chair. "Grandpa should drink a whole cupful!"

Abigail turned to Tammy with questioning eyes. "When is Keith's dad coming? It will be nice to see him again."

"He will be arriving in a few weeks," she replied. "Since he is the mission treasurer and works from the States, he visits Congo from time to time to check up on us and conduct business meetings and things like that."

"We are also expecting two more visitors—Allen and Jessica Smith," Keith added. "We've mentioned them before, but I don't think you've met them, Chris and Abby. They are a nice young couple—both doctors—and they plan to start a hospital here in Kisangani."

"Which reminds me," Tammy began. "We're not sure where to house them during their first few days here. The clinic building is a mess, and we may not have it prepared by the time they arrive."

"We would be happy to house them," Abigail volunteered, knowing that her husband would be on the same page. "We are probably the only family on campus with the extra space, as you know."

When supper was over and the children's bedtime arrived, the families parted. The younger couple sensed a change in the breeze as they tramped home across the campus drive and up the path to their quiet brick house.

"This morning feels like it was forever ago," Abigail exclaimed as she slipped off her shoes and jumped behind her mosquito net. "It was quite the journey over the river and through the jungle today. Kayumba must be thrilled that we made it back tonight."

Christopher chuckled. "I'm sure he is. As soon as we put the motorcycles away for the night, he was hightailing it to his house. I think we're all pretty glad that we survived the trip in one piece."

CHAPTER 7

ARRIVALS

After sifting through the seemingly endless material of her mosquito net for an opening, Abigail stumbled out of bed.

"I am feeling incredibly sore and sunburned this morning," she announced to Christopher, then winced as her shoulder brushed against the rough mahogany door trim. "Remind me again why we have mahogany doors and trim?"

Christopher warily eyed the cold shower water spraying in their bathroom as he replied. "Because it's the cheapest wood available here."

Abigail paused in the doorway. "Haven't you been standing in front of that shower for the last ten minutes?"

Christopher grinned sheepishly. "It's just—so very cold."

"The water isn't getting any warmer," she teased. "I prefer to take my shower midday when the cool water feels refreshing in the damp heat."

"I'm not doing that."

"Suit yourself."

As Christopher contemplated his shower, Abigail unlocked their wooden front door leading to the porch, stepped out, and began to cook breakfast. Pancakes had quickly become a favorite, paired with honey Keith brought from Tanzania. The simplicity of the missionary's recipe was astounding—just a mixture of two flours, sugar, and water. Abigail felt it was God's blessing that produced the fluffy, bubbling cakes over the charcoal or gas burners each morning.

Working in the printing container once again that morning, Abigail cut the uneven edges of a children's Sabbath School songbook in Swahili. The paper cutter made even slices as she mechanically lifted the metal cutting lever and then pulled it down. Each time she pulled, she grimaced because of muscle soreness from her long motorcycle ride several days before.

"I had planned for another well-drilling trip next week," Nathan announced, clearing his throat as he suddenly entered the container. "I know that I mentioned it to Christopher earlier this morning. But Daniel is coughing and crying with asthmatic attacks all through the night. Until we figure out the cause of the problem, Starla and I can't risk being deep in the jungle without some medical support."

"That's understandable," Abigail replied, nodding and feeling relieved that she was blessed with more time to recover from their last expedition. "Maybe the Smiths can offer some ideas when they visit."

"Maybe so." The contemplative expression on Nathan's face lifted for a moment. "How is the printing process going?" The two discussed the printing projects for a few minutes before Nathan exited.

The noon hour came and went. Keith and the box cruiser had barreled out of the campus drive en route to the airport in Kisangani to pick up the guests. Alvina busily traveled back and forth between the Rittenour and Mosier homes, transporting pots and pans in the stroller, preparing for a large evening meal of beans, potatoes, and cabbage.

Several hours later, Abigail wandered over to the Mosiers' to meet the newly arrived guests.

"Ah, how are you this afternoon Abigail?" Pastor Mtenzi's deep-brown eyes smiled down on her as they both paused by the back porch. The Tanzanian had recently returned from an evangelism trip in the bush.

"I'm doing well, thank you," she responded.

When evangelistic efforts in Congo had taken shape nearly ten years before, Msifiri Mtenzi was among the first to join Keith Mosier on the venture. Although he had acquired a few more gray hairs since that day, he still walked with a quiet, commanding presence. He and his wife—an unpretentious woman with good cooking skills—lived on campus in one of the brick houses that surrounded the palm tree circle.

Mtenzi's eyes twinkled. "I, too, have come to see our guests today."

The Mosiers and Rittenours had already gathered around the wooden kitchen table when Abigail crossed the threshold.

"Welcome!" Tammy didn't miss a beat as she picked up Talitha from the cement floor to place her in a high chair.

Abigail quickly saw that a pair of unexpected visitors had arrived on campus. Elder Tembo and his wife, Unity, originated from Tanzania but had been on an evangelism trip to Kindu, DRC, where Congo Frontline Missions was overseeing outreach. They were a watchful, quiet Tanzanian couple with few words to add above the general chatter at the table.

"Tell me, brother," Pastor Mtenzi inquired warmly of the newcomer from his homeland. "How was it in Kindu?"

The middle-aged man's eyes momentarily brightened. "We were seeing great success there. Many people came to our evangelistic training and were encouraged. Sadly, rebel activity began to increase in the area, and we heard that they were on their way to Kindu. We were forced to cut our training short to avoid the danger."

"Ah." Mtenzi breathed deeply. "Have we heard any news yet to confirm that rebels did invade the area?"

Elder Tembo nodded. "They arrived not long after our plane took off."

"Kisangani has remained peaceful overall, though, hasn't it?" It was Allen Smith, another newcomer, who glanced up from a plate of rice and potatoes to interject his question.

"We are very blessed to live in a politically stable area," Keith answered. "But election time usually feels questionable, no matter where we are in Congo."

"Until the Congolese people become of one heart, I do not think we will see much change," Pastor Mtenzi added, shaking his head solemnly. "We are a divided country."

Allen pushed his chair back from the table and rubbed his belly. "Thank you for the wonderful meal, Tammy."

Turning from the quiet Mr. and Mrs. Tembo to bright-eyed Allen and Jessica Smith, Abigail studied the two young doctors. Allen appeared to be of French and English descent, with tall stature and dark hair curling in waves over his forehead. His posture was erect and commanding for his thirty or so years. As he ran his fingers through a close-cropped beard, he answered questions around the table confidently. While the doctor had a somewhat crusty exterior, Abigail sensed that he had a soft heart.

Allen clearly adored his wife of six years. He watched her admiringly as she knelt on the cement floor to converse with young Caleb Mosier. "Don't worry, your boo-boo will be just fine," she assured him, patting his knee. Her soft smile and sweetness of voice were like bread and butter to the four-year-old's soul. With a fresh burst of energy, Caleb jumped up and raced to join Shiloh on the porch swing just outside.

Jessica pulled her dark curls back at the nape of her neck as she straightened and turned to her adventurer husband. Being originally from the Dominican Republic, her skin was a lovely sun-kissed shade of light tan.

Starla cleared her throat and spoke to Allen. "I hope that before you and Jessica leave us, you can give Nathan and me an opinion on Daniel's lungs. We have inhalers from the States to use in a real emergency, but his breathing seems strained, especially when sleeping in our house. Ever since he contracted pneumonia in the bush, his lungs have not been the same."

"Where is Daniel now?" Jessica's gaze flitted across the room.

"He is napping here in one of the bedrooms," Starla replied, nodding toward a wooden door nearby. "His lungs seem to do better away from our house."

"Have you checked for mold?" Allen asked quickly.

"Nathan has his suspicions."

The whir of a four-wheeler sounded in the yard. "It's Chris!" Caleb shouted from the porch. "He's here to get the suitcases!"

"Thank you so much for opening your home to us," Jessica said gratefully to Abigail. "Tammy told me that we are staying with you and your husband."

"It's our pleasure." Abigail nodded as Allen lugged several large handbags out to the porch. Now that she had swept the termite sawdust and scampering lizards out of the room, the unused space would be perfect for the couple.

The Dumans were curious to learn more about this couple. The Smiths were travelers, having just recently flown to Congo from somewhere in the Middle East. Previous to their adventures there, Allen was flying a plane in Alaska and firing shots from his gun to scare away approaching grizzlies.

"I really think Allen is not afraid of anything," Jessica remarked with a smile after a short recap of their travels. "Well . . ." she paused. "He says that he's afraid of heights."

"He's afraid of heights and flies planes?" Chris queried.

She rolled her eyes. "Yeah, I question his sanity myself."

Allen grinned. "I hold to a strong belief that fears should be conquered."

The next morning, Abigail set to work early in her garden plot across from the Rittenours'. Taking a hoe leaning against a pile of composted brush, she began to uproot weeds from a long row of tender green bean plants. It was a beautiful morning. The soft sounds of Alvina gently singing to Daniel traveled on the mild breeze. Water gushed from an outdoor spigot nearby as Mamma Rebecca began a load of washing. Happy shouts erupted from the strong-walled depot where several campus employees conversed.

Don't forget the books in the printing container. Abigail paused mid-hoe with the mental reminder. The rainy season was soon to dump buckets of water across Kisangani, and the weeds in the garden would be out of control at that point. But she didn't have unlimited time, and printing the books was a greater priority. "I'd better begin printing," Abigail murmured.

Nathan and Kayumba had already dragged the large generator out from behind the container in preparation for her work. With some uncertainty, Abigail tried the starter, then nodded with satisfaction when the big square machine bellowed to life. With the printer warming up and the air conditioner shooting out jets of cool air, she packed sets of small printed books into boxes. Every half hour, Abigail glanced at her wristwatch to keep track of the time.

That evening marked the beginning of a week of prayer in the campus chapel. Keith, ever the opportunist, jumped at the impromptu arrival of the Tembos. "We need a revival on campus," Keith had announced.

The sound of singing coming from the classroom chapel drew people from their gardens and homes at the end of the day. "Let's take this shortcut," Christopher suggested as he turned to venture from the gravel road toward the campus center.

Abigail eyed the tall, thick clumps of grass before them. "Just keep a lookout for snakes."

Mamma Rebecca and her husband were already sitting on a wooden bench at the back of the chapel when the couple arrived. Kayumba, having slipped inside with his wife, Esther, and their children, leafed through the pages of a songbook while he balanced a child on one knee. Mamma Rose must have heard the news from where she lived in Huit—for she too sat with her silent baby tied expertly on her back in a colorful sling of local material.

"I'd like to share a story with you this evening," Elder Tembo began after the notes of the last song died away. "A story about a man who was my enemy." Even the children sat quietly and listened as the gentle man continued.

While working at a mission school in Tanzania, Tembo faced strong opposition from a certain man who sought to destroy his reputation and influence.

"One day, my enemy grew very sick," he said. "A terrible sore developed on his body, and the stench of it drove his friends and relatives away from his house. Only his wife stayed with him. The man's family guessed that he would die and did not offer to take care of him or transport him to the hospital for treatment. They just left and waited for the end to come."

When Tembo heard the news, he took a deep breath and determined to visit his adversary on a mission of mercy—but not before the dying man's relatives met him with a cold warning. "If you do anything to help him and he still dies, you will pay for his funeral expenses." Rubbing their hands together in satisfaction, they looked pleased—funeral expenses would include a hefty sum that they would be happy to escape.

"Should I take the risk?" Tembo questioned. "If I should try to help, and this man were to die anyway, I did not have the money to pay for his funeral. But as a Christian, I knew that I should love my neighbor and especially my enemy. I knew what the Lord wanted me to do."

Tembo chose to take the risk. "The stench was nauseating when I entered the house. It was all I could do not to run for fresh, pure air," he recounted to the listeners in the chapel. "But I approached the man's bed and offered to clean his wound. Once I had done all that I knew to do, I took him to the hospital for medical treatment and paid for his bills there.

"My enemy made a complete recovery. When he and I returned by motorbike to the area, the news traveled that I had returned. The man's family—assuming that he had died—gathered at my house, where I found them waiting to join me for the funeral service."

Surprise and shock registered on the faces of the relatives when the man they had left to die assured them that he was quite well and that he did not anticipate his own funeral for some time.

"You are no longer my family," Tembo's old enemy announced with conviction. "This man—the one who took care of me—he is my family."

"From that day forward," Tembo closed his message, "this man became my brother. He saw that his relatives did not have a true love for him. Instead, he saw that God used the man he hated to save his life, and that love warmed his heart.

"Love your enemies," the Tanzanian said and then paused as his message drew to a close. "Do good to those who hate and persecute you."

The room had become very silent, except for the occasional creak of a wooden bench and a gust of wind rattling the window shutters as a storm brewed outside.

"I do not know what challenges lie ahead for each one of you. Maybe you have enemies who wish you harm. But listen to the words of Jesus and His love," Tembo urged. "This love is powerful enough to make all of us family."

The meeting closed with prayer, and people raced across the campus circle amid splattering raindrops. Elder Tembo was not a prophet, but his words strengthened many hearts for the days ahead.

CHAPTER 8

SNAKES AND REBELS

The Dumans were tracing the familiar path home after a pleasant worship hour in the Mosiers' living room when dusky shadows began to play tricks on Abigail's eyes.

"It's just a stick, Abby." Christopher's observant eye had caught her pausing to identify a coiled vine on the gravel drive.

"I know. It's not a snake," Abigail replied.

"Someone's jumpy," he teased.

The house stood quiet and dark in the grassy clearing. Christopher turned the key in the lock of their mahogany front door and murmured, "I need to replace this door with an American one from storage."

"Why is that?" Abigail asked as she reached for her cell phone lying on their makeshift bookcase.

"Keith said that this door isn't very secure. It would be better to have something more solid for security."

"Speaking of security, do you know what time Allen and Jessica are return-ing tonight?" Abigail now called out from the spare bedroom where she hunted for a cell-phone-battery charging bank.

Christopher—having settled himself under the mosquito net with one of Keith's books—looked up. "I'm not sure. I know they took a boat across the river to treat some locals with medical needs today."

As she crouched barefoot on the cool cement floor of the nearby bedroom, Abigail grasped the charging cord and pulled the battery bank from the solar panel on the wall. "I'm surprised that they haven't returned yet. It's not safe to travel the road at this time of night."

"Allen and Jessica either don't realize or don't mind. Probably the latter," Christopher said matter-of-factly.

Being careful of the potatoes stored on the cool cement floor, Abigail shuffled through the darkness with bare feet until she reached the living room. Then, sinking into a locally made chair of woven vines to curl up in a fuzzy blanket from the United States, she breathed a sigh of contentment.

"I'm going to call my mom in a minute."

Something made Christopher lay aside his book and part the cloud of mosquito netting above him. Abigail was so interested in talking to her mother about the events of the week that she scarcely heard the click of his flashlight as the bright beams suddenly illuminated the floor.

"And *that* is a snake," came the slow, deliberate words. "Don't move—stay right where you are."

Abigail pulled her legs up to her chest and looked in the direction of the light. Slithering slowly across the cement floor was a small black snake.

Christopher killed it quickly with a machete he kept by his bedside. "I wonder what kind it is," he pondered as he flung the limp reptile into the tall grasses outside. "By the way—I hear the voices of Allen and Jessica on the campus drive. They must have arrived earlier and eaten at Mamma Mtenzi's."

The more seasoned missionaries on campus could not determine whether the intruder was a harmless house snake or a cobra. The next morning, Abigail sat on a bench in their bedroom for several minutes, pondering her close call. "How many times have I walked over these floors in the dark at night with no light?" she mused aloud. "Only a few minutes before that black snake emerged from the storage room, I had shuffled over the same area in bare feet."

Her heart felt touched by God's mercy as she prepared for the approaching Sabbath. *The Lord truly does look after us.*

As Allen discussed plans for future medical work with Keith at the office that morning, Jessica offered to help with the cooking for the usual potluck at the Mosiers' home the next day.

"Thank you so much again for housing us," she repeatedly sweetly. "Keith and Tammy mentioned that in a week or so, we should be able to move into the empty clinic on the campus green."

Her new friend smiled. "We're happy to have the company, but I'm sure that you'll be happy to have your own place on campus."

That Sabbath, the church service was held in the chapel. Afterward, the missionaries gathered at the Mosier home for a potluck of rice, beans, and potatoes. They enjoyed the good company before scattering for the afternoon.

Abigail sensed that the Mosier family was especially tired from a long week. Tammy reclined on the couch as little Talitha snoozed nearby under a small mosquito net. Anna lay on the living room mat and clutched a stuffed animal in her chubby fingers as she traced the path of a lizard across the ceiling. The redness under her eyes told of a forbidden dip into the peanut butter at lunch. She had moved too quickly for Tammy to intervene this time.

"Why don't we take a walk?" Christopher suggested. "The heat isn't so oppressive this afternoon."

SNAKES AND REBELS

Abigail nodded and took hold of his hand. They passed Kayumba's house and waved to Esther, where she sat on the porch and nursed their smallest child. The office building stood locked and empty that afternoon, but the guard's house at the corner by the gate buzzed with activity as children played with a few makeshift toys in the yard. Mamma Nikke, the Mosiers' helper on weekdays, lived here with her husband, Leon, who patrolled campus at night in shifts with several other men.

When the young couple reached the campus entrance, the swinging metal gate was already open. As they rounded a bend in the long, sandy driveway, Abigail shook the dust and pebbles from her sandals and looked up to see a sweet scene before them.

Starla Rittenour's hands rested on a stroller as sunny-natured Daniel cackled with delight at a pile of sand by the side of the driveway. Nathan crouched nearby, letting the tiny gold grains slip through his calloused fingers.

"Look here, Daniel, let's make a castle." The father laughed as his little son's grin spread from ear to ear.

Starla called out when she spotted the Dumans approaching. "I hear that you met with a snake the other day."

Chris laughed. "Yes, although we are not sure whether it was poisonous or not. I killed it anyway."

"When in question, stay on the safe side," Nathan warned. "Some of the snakes here are deadly."

"Of course, the Bible workers and church planters we send out after evangelism training deal with snakes of a whole different sort," his wife volunteered, tucking a wisp of dark hair behind her ear.

A contemplative expression passed over Nathan's face. Abigail recognized the look. It always indicated that beyond his quiet exterior, the wheels of his mind were puzzling over something much deeper, processing some perplexing problem.

In a few moments, Nathan spoke again. "The Bible workers we sponsor give us reports from their territories. Some of them will be bicycling along a trail and suddenly see a large serpent coiled around the handlebars. It's a demonic manifestation."

"What happens then?" Abigail asked him.

"From what our frontline workers tell us, prayer is always the first resort. After a word of prayer, the snakes dissolve into thin air."

"Wow," she breathed.

Starla spoke up. "Pastor Mtenzi heard another report too: a church planter was on his bicycle, and a large snake suddenly slithered out of his pant leg. It was such a strange, unexplainable occurrence that the man knew exactly what

59

he was dealing with. These men truly live by faith. They realize that their only safety is found in God."

"And, I'm sure, they realize that resting in His will is the safest place to be," Abigail added with a tone of personal reflection.

Nathan switched topics with little more than a nod. "I forgot to tell you, Chris, that the education inspector for the area stopped by the school this week. He was very approving of the new well there. The man told me that we have 'good hearts' for placing the well close to the road so that passersby can benefit."

"That's good to hear," Christopher nodded.

"We don't always receive such positive feedback for our efforts," Starla added.

Nathan chuckled. "Yes, some people remain suspicious. They will find one thing or another to complain about. And if nothing else, there is always another area in need of a well that we haven't drilled yet. For some, our efforts are never good enough."

"We can only do what we can do," Chris responded, shrugging.

"At least we don't have to deal with the same roadblocks that others have faced—such as the Tembos did in Kindu," Abigail suggested. "In the form of rebels."

The cloud of thoughtfulness again settled over Nathan's face. "The rebels are a force to be taken seriously."

"Who are they, exactly?" Her curiosity could not be helped. She patiently tried to wait as Nathan hesitated for several moments in his thoughtful reverie.

"They are people who protest against the government but often in ways that are violent toward both soldiers and civilians. Some groups are especially terrible. The Mai-Mai are one such group because they mix their war tactics with spiritualism." Even Daniel looked up from his sand pile to gaze into the serious face of his young father.

Nathan continued, "The Mai-Mai engage in spiritualistic routines before they enter into serious conflict. It's been said that soldiers with the Congolese government have emptied their AKs with round after round of ammunition at the charging Mai-Mai, only to watch bullets bounce off the rebel forms." A slight smile formed on Nathan's lips. "Can you imagine how disgruntled the soldiers were to see that bullets had no effect? They have good reason to be afraid!"

The whirring of a motorcycle on the road nearby interrupted Daniel's play. "Safe, safe?" the little one choked out as an expression of fear clouded his blue eyes.

"Yes, you're safe," Starla told her son, hugging him close.

"The war between good and evil is real," Abigail remarked. "We wrestle not against flesh and blood."

The Dumans left the Rittenours playing with Daniel in the sand.

Abigail reached for Christopher's arm as they again passed through the campus gate. "I'm thankful that even in the presence of snakes and rebels, we can recognize God's power over all things." She tipped her hat back to let the sunshine in and squeezed his arm. "Nathan's stories also remind me that if the devil can provide his followers with protection—like shielding the Mai-Mai from bullets—God can do much more to shield His children from evil."

CHAPTER 9

MOLD AND FIRE

Before Allen and Jessica carried the last of their belongings from the spare bedroom at the Dumans' house to the clinic by the green, the two couples took a walk together down to the roadside at the Barry Mosier school.

"We loved staying at your house," Jessica's said, her pretty face beaming. "I'm so glad that we could meet over here in Congo."

"It is amazing to see how God works to bring friends together, even overseas," Abigail replied with a smile.

When the small group reached the schoolyard, Allen clamped his large, tan hand down on a windowsill and turned to Christopher. "These are pretty nice buildings."

Because it was Sunday, the buildings were empty. The dirt schoolyard seemed lonely to Abigail—lonely without Mamma Rose, her little toddler Josiah, and all the school children. The men studied the mound where the new well stood, almost complete now. "Maybe we can finish this one of these days when Nathan has his house problem figured out," Christopher remarked.

Jessica lingered behind the small group, capturing photos of plants, flowers, and bugs along the way with her camera. "Look! A locust." She reached for her camera again.

Allen didn't skip a beat. "Wow, let's eat it. Where's a lighter?"

Abigail looked up with concern. "Oh no."

"Why, you don't want to eat it?" She noticed a teasing glint in his eye.

"I only eat the plant variety."

While Allen seemed to enjoy the ripples of reaction he created with his outlandish comments, he did have a serious side. On their return to the campus, he and Christopher talked in serious tones as the women chattered.

An unusual stir began that week at the Rittenour home. After conducting a thorough search, Nathan found that his suspicions were warranted—Congo's extreme humidity and a leak beneath the bathtub had bred a serious mold problem. Nathan placed well drilling and even booklet printing on hold in an effort to renovate quickly, as poor Daniel coughed and cried at night, leaving

Starla pale and drained. Day by day, picking up where Nathan had left off, Abigail worked in the printing container, attempting to carry on with any task that she could.

That Tuesday morning, Nathan paused as he passed the Dumans' porch. "I've put well drilling on hold for right now, and I believe that we should be thinking about doing repair work on the road to Kisangani," he suggested. "With the rainy season almost upon us, I'm afraid that the road will become nearly impassable without our intervention. It will be difficult enough to reach town in our regular vehicles, never mind the big well-drilling rig when it arrives."

"Who normally maintains the road?" Abigail asked innocently, pausing her dish washing in the outdoor sink.

"Anyone with the equipment, time, and desire," Nathan responded quickly. "Another reason to take responsibility for the road is to discourage the thievery that happens at night."

"How so?" Abigail scraped the remnants of the morning's fried potatoes from a cooking pan.

"Because of the potholes and washouts, motorcyclists are forced to drive slowly. Thieves take advantage of the opportunity. If we can dig drainage ditches and smooth the road with our Bobcat, the motorcyclists can drive faster and potentially avoid being stopped."

"That sounds well worth the effort," Christopher remarked as he finished lacing up his work boots. "When shall we start? I can't say that I love driving that crazy old Bobcat, but it would be great to help the community."

"We should begin on the next good day of weather when the roads are dry. Remind me to give you a letter to carry when you are out on the road. Clearing trees along the road can be a tricky thing if they are valuable and owned by locals."

"What's the worst that could happen if I did knock over an oil palm?" Christopher asked in a rare moment of curiosity.

"Let's see; the owner calculates the total value that the one oil palm could have produced in oil for the next thirty years. And then you are charged that amount of money."

"Wow. What does this letter do for me?"

"We received special written permission from authorities in town to cut trees that are too close to the road if needed. While we still need to be careful, this saves us from a lot of potential trouble."

Nathan left to tackle more home renovations while Christopher tracked down Kayumba for his help with several campus maintenance projects—one being the installation of a loud siren at Keith's house. The missionary hoped that if robbers visited his house, the loud noise might throw them off guard.

Christopher had worked for an hour when the average lazy afternoon suddenly turned into a mad scramble. One of the campus guards had sounded an alert over a hand-held radio. Kayumba stood by Christopher's side and listened to the message. Bernard had spotted a thin trail of smoke coming from an area of tall grasses along the winding campus driveway.

Christopher, Kayumba, and another campus worker jumped into the nearby Land Cruiser and took off toward the smoke. In a brief minute, the small group pulled up to the area. The tall grasses near the sand pile where Daniel Rittenour loved to play were ablaze.

"*Moto*," Kayumba coughed out the obvious: "Fire." He waved his hand before his face dramatically as the gentle breeze ruffled his T-shirt sleeve. "Come and help!" He motioned toward two good Samaritans who ran to join them from the main road.

"How can we put this fire out?" Christopher asked. They were far from the well in the center of campus, and the well in the schoolyard wasn't functional yet. Christopher watched as his Congolese friend hacked palm fronds off from a nearby tree with a machete. He handed one to each of the men.

Whack! Kayumba thumped the outskirts of the fire with the branch. Surprisingly, the impact had a dampening effect on the flames.

In some areas of the spreading fire, flames extended above Christopher's height of six feet and consumed small trees. The group's efforts to contain the fire would have been a losing battle except that the breeze died. No longer contending with the wind, the men were able to beat out the flames. Thirty minutes later, they surveyed the charred and smoking ground before them.

Christopher pulled the Land Cruiser through the gate just as Keith firmly shut the office door behind him. "How did the firefighting go?"

As the two men conversed, the question of what started the fire came up.

"Oh, probably just a spark from a cigarette." Keith looked especially logical as he locked the office door. "A motorcyclist passing by probably tossed it into the bush and didn't think twice."

"All's well that ends well," Christopher responded. "Are you done with work for the day?"

Keith nodded. "Yes, I promised the kids that I would give them a motorcycle ride this afternoon."

Chris went home to change into fresh clothes. Soon, the rumble of Keith's white Yamaha echoed across the campus. The Mosier kids giggled happily, clinging to their daddy's back as he carefully maneuvered between various houses and occasionally paused to chat jovially with the locals.

"Hi, Mr. Allen and Jessica!" Shiloh called in singsong as they reached the clinic building. The young couple had moved in the last of their belongings.

MOLD AND FIRE

"Hello!" Jessica smiled and waved from the porch, where she was hanging a clothesline between the support columns.

"You're invited to popcorn, smoothies, and worship this evening at our house," Keith told her, smiling.

While the young Mosiers meandered through papaya gardens and over well-worn paths around the campus, Nathan Rittenour set out from his house to the Dumans with a purposeful stride. As Abigail watched him approach from the porch, she could see an expression of concern on his face.

Marching up to the porch, he reached for a support post and wasted no time getting to the point of his visit. "Can Starla, Daniel, and I come to live with you for a while? I don't know how long it will be." He plunged ahead. "Maybe several weeks, maybe a month. The mold in our house is bothering all of us, and now it appears that all of the floors will need to be replaced."

Christopher and Abigail exchanged glances. Although this would make round two of the company they had entertained this month, they wouldn't think of refusing. "Of course, that would be fine," Chris said.

"Very well," Nathan replied, nodding. "And thank you. We will begin moving our things over soon. Alvina will be coming with us as well."

When Nathan had gone, Abigail slowly rose from a stool and looked at her husband. "I guess we have some things to get ready here at the house this evening."

The storage room (where the solar equipment powering the house was kept) would be Alvina's place to sleep. Chris stored wiring, tools, and suitcases in the room, and Abigail used it as a potato pantry. While Christopher tackled the various tasks there, Abigail set out to baby-proof the living area for little Daniel. When they were finished, the house looked ready—but even more adjustments were required when Starla arrived on the scene.

"Can we remove some of the locally crafted furniture from the living room?" she asked. "The dust and mold on the mats and chairs tend to bother my respiratory system," she admitted.

"Of course." Abigail picked up a mat from the floor and rolled it onto the cement porch. *Although I might have a few more inconveniences in future days, I realize that this family has had to undergo the greater inconvenience*, she thought.

When the Rittenours arrived at the Dumans' home, Abigail learned that Mamma Rebecca came as part of a package deal. The pleasant Congolese woman arrived for duty each weekday morning. She was a slightly plump woman with a toothy grin and a quiet spirit. Abigail often observed her passing the time in song. Every day of the week except for Sabbath, she sported a rag or kerchief tied around her head with a knot and was constantly on the lookout for areas where she could help in the kitchen and around the house.

One day, as Abigail and Rebecca were working on preparations for lunch together in the outdoor kitchen, Abigail was chopping a head of green cabbage. When she reached the hard, inner-core of the vegetable, she tossed it into a compost bucket on the cement floor nearby.

Mamma Rebecca spied her spontaneous act. She reached down into the bucket and fished the cabbage core out. "Are you not going to use the rest of this?" she asked in Swahili.

Abigail's efforts to practice Swahili were beginning to pay off. Although she spoke slowly, she felt sure of her word choices. "You can keep it if you want," she replied.

She watched as the woman pulled an earth-toned sack from the folds of her skirt and carefully placed the cabbage core inside along with several other kitchen scraps. They would undoubtedly go into a pot for her supper that evening.

Abigail usually prided herself on being thrifty. Even in the United States, she minimized food waste and lived frugally. But in light of Mamma Rebecca reclaiming what she had considered compost, the American now had some "food for thought."

The lighthearted sounds of children's voices suddenly greeted the two on the porch. Five Congolese boys ran up a nearby path to Bernard's house. Several of them were Bernard's boys, enjoying a favorite pastime—a game of carefully guiding old rubber tires with sticks in front of their sandaled feet.

A few moments later, Abigail spotted the familiar figure of Tammy Mosier on the mission driveway. Caleb, Anna, and Shiloh ran ahead as she pushed a stroller containing Talitha.

"We wanted to pay you a visit," Tammy said as she smiled and reached to pull her youngest from the stroller.

"I'm so glad that you did," Abigail replied, smiling back. The Mosier household was such a busy one that Tammy rarely seemed to leave for social visits.

"Where are the Rittenours?"

"Oh, Alvina is out on a walk right now. Nathan is at work in his house, and Starla has taken Daniel for a stroll."

Mamma Rebecca, seeing the visitors, washed the final dish in the kitchen sink and waved goodbye as she left with her worn sack of vegetable scraps tucked into her skirt.

Abigail turned from the disappearing Rebecca to Tammy, who sat beside her on the porch. "The concept of having hired help seems foreign to me," she murmured. "I feel better about doing the work myself as opposed to hiring a local to do it for me, and I wouldn't have a helper here except that she is employed by Nathan and Starla."

"I know that it feels strange at first, and people in the United States might not understand," Tammy admitted. "But by providing these local ladies with a job on campus, we are actually passing on a great blessing." Tammy paused, watching her children sift through sand piles in the shade of several bushy oil palms. "Working in the fields is much more physically taxing on the women, and it does not provide as much income as they receive working for us."

"You're saying that while we benefit from their help, they are also benefiting?" Abigail received a handful of sand from Talitha's toddler fingers.

"Yes. You'll grow more accustomed to it. Having a good helper can be a wonderful blessing—just so long as she is an honest one."

Abigail raised an eyebrow inquisitively. "It sounds like you've had experience in that area."

Tammy nodded. "Before Mamma Nikke began working for us, we had another woman worker. Over time, I noticed items disappearing from around the house but figured that maybe the children or I had misplaced them. And then one day, my favorite blue skirt disappeared off of the clothesline." She paused. "This skirt was very special to me for its sentimental value when I was first getting to know Keith. Although I searched and searched for the skirt, it never showed up."

"What happened?"

"We ended up letting my woman worker go because it became apparent that she was stealing. We asked her to return the items that she had stolen, and she complied to an extent, but my blue skirt was not among the things she returned. A few weeks later, Keith and I were driving to Kisangani when a familiar flash of blue caught my attention: it was our previous worker, walking along the dirt road wearing my favorite blue skirt. Even though seeing my stolen skirt was such a small thing, I struggled to keep from feeling upset."

"I would feel rather violated in such a situation," Abigail replied.

"I felt that way at first," she admitted. "I would have happily given her a skirt to wear if she needed one. But you come to realize that in this life, things are just things. I'm thankful for the good memories I have and for the character development I've gained through the process of little trials. I may have lost some possessions along the way, but I've gained much more in lessons learned."

Caleb steered a toy truck through Shiloh's carefully planned castle moat just then. "No, Caleb!" the older child protested.

"Caleb, drive your truck in the other corner of the sandpile," Tammy told him, motioning in that direction.

Abigail was inspired by Tammy's forgiving spirit. "Are people here never taught that stealing is wrong?" the younger woman asked thoughtfully.

"Oh, some know that it's wrong. Through reading Scripture and the conviction of the Holy Spirit, they understand that to take what doesn't belong to them is stealing. But culturally, stealing is very acceptable and isn't even considered stealing. In fact, some figure that if we knew how much they needed the laundry on our clothesline or the food in our kitchen, we would give it to them happily. What we call 'stealing,' they call 'borrowing.' Because that attitude is a part of the culture here, we missionaries try to help locals do the right thing by minimizing their temptation to take from us."

"Is this why the porches to our homes have cages around them?"

"For that reason, and for security from robbers," she said quietly. Keith and Tammy avoided conversations with references to danger around the children. Shiloh was very sharp for her age and kept her ear tuned for interesting adult conversations.

The two women turned just in time to see Talitha squatting by a bowl of cucumbers on the porch and taking a bite from the largest one. "Oh no, Talitha," Tammy exclaimed as she retrieved her little one. "I'm sorry."

She returned to her previous train of thought. "We had one former missionary who routinely left laptops and other electronics out in plain view and within easy access to sticky fingers. It's a wonder that none were stolen. Kayumba would only shake his head and report it to Keith with the reminder that such a habit was risky."

"Kayumba seems like a really genuine man," Abigail remarked. "I know that Chris enjoys working with him."

"I believe that Kayumba has been working for us longer than any of the others on campus," Tammy explained. "We have kept him on—not because he is perfect and hasn't made mistakes—but he has exhibited humility and a willingness to be honest with us and help the work."

"Have you had to 'let go' a lot of workers in the past?"

"Yes. A fair amount, actually. Our main workers represent us to the community on various projects, so we prefer to find truly Christian families who do not steal and are faithful to their marriage vows. Many appear upstanding to begin with, but time reveals weaknesses that we cannot support. All of this," she said as she gestured to the campus grounds, "has been paid for and supported by donors for the Lord's work. It's a responsibility we have to take seriously."

"That makes sense." Abigail nodded and wiped a growing heap of sand from her brightly colored wrap skirt.

"One of our past workers still lives nearby in Huit," the missionary wife remarked. "He goes by the name of 'Prence.' And although he is short of stature, he sure carries himself like one. He fed our dog in the mornings and took care of chores around the house expertly. But in time, we were compelled to lay him off because of his dishonesty. He still acts like he is very bitter about it, and Keith feels sorry."

Abigail shrugged. "I know that Keith loves to be on good terms with everyone here, but there's not much more one can do."

Tammy straightened. "Talitha!"

The chubby little girl emerged from the open doorway of the house. As she toddled over, a trail of corn flour followed her. Tammy coaxed open her little fist. "Let's go before we do further damage to Abby's food supply," she said with a laugh. "Shiloh, Caleb, Anna—it's time to go home now."

The following morning, Mamma Rebecca returned to the Dumans' home neatly dressed and cheerful. As the local woman busied herself around the house, Abigail watched her with a new attitude—thanks to her conversation with Tammy. She began to grow fond of her cheerful, humble spirit and felt at liberty to practice her language learning skills with her, feeling that the woman wouldn't look down on her for her mistakes.

After practicing a phrase from her Swahili textbook on the living room couch, Abigail emerged into the outdoor kitchen and broke out in Swahili.

Mamma Rebecca's eyes brightened, and her face melted into a smile. She repeated the words with slightly different intonation. Her encouragement pressed Abigail to continue learning the language. It soon came in handy when Starla delivered special instructions in English to her helper that afternoon. Although Rebecca looked happy to oblige, her face took on a blank look. She turned to Abigail questioningly, who explained in broken Swahili. Wonderfully, Rebecca seemed to understand.

"I am so thankful that we have Mamma Rebecca to work for us," Starla remarked that evening, placing a blender full of smoothie on a nearby table as Daniel smacked his lips. "She is so sweet and good-hearted."

"I can see why you are glad," Abigail agreed with a deeper understanding. "Tammy shared some insights with me yesterday that helped me to see how we all help each other. An honest and trustworthy companion in daily labor is such a treasure!"

Reflecting on the events of the busy week—the Smiths' youthful sense of adventure, Rittenours' terrible mold problem, the random fire set on campus property, and Tammy's story about her stolen blue skirt—Abigail scrawled a few sentences down in her journal. "The missionaries here have my utmost respect," she wrote. "They accept inconvenience and challenges without complaint."

CHAPTER 10

TRIALS

Abigail and Christopher woke in the middle of the night to a single clap of thunder. Bucket loads of rain pounded on the metal roof of the brick house.

"Chris, I'm feeling misty sprays on my face."

"Welcome to the beginning of the rainy season. It's from the cement bricks near the ceiling—or cracks along the shutters. Maybe I should check."

Reaching for a headlamp under his pillow, Christopher sent a beam around the walls of the room to reveal a dreary sight.

"It appears that rain has soaked through the brick," Abigail observed, blinking incredulously in the bright light.

"Not only that, but it's coursing down the cracks in the wooden shutters, even though they are closed."

"What can we do?"

"There's not much that we can do right now. You didn't leave our books on the floor before we went to bed, did you? I see puddles on the cement."

Abigail gasped. She parted the mosquito netting and reached down to pick up a stack of their mission storybooks from the floor. Abigail sighed. "One book has a few wet pages, but the others appear dry."

"We will have to deal with the rest of this mess in the morning. We've got to fix the road to town . . ." Christopher's voice trailed off into a sleepy mumble.

At morning's light, the smell of damp floor mats and soaked clothes permeated the small bedroom. Abigail reached for a mat and gingerly dragged it out to the porch to air dry. Meanwhile, Chris took a broom and literally swept the water out through the front door. Although they had only two precious towels to their name in Africa, both were used to dry the floor and tossed into a laundry hamper. "Let's hope that the sun comes out to dry the clothes that I'll need to wash today," Abigail remarked.

The other bedrooms were not as heavily flooded with water, but lingering dampness clung to the walls and permeated the air like a cloud. Several days later, Abigail noticed dark spots appearing on her bedroom wall beneath one of the windows and guessed that it was mold. Try as she did to scrub it with any abrasive cleaner she could find on hand, the ugly spots never disappeared.

The Rittenours had a similar problem on their bedroom walls, although the spots were less pronounced. Nathan and Starla decided to move their bedroom outside to the porch, where the fresh air was in abundance and they were still protected from outside dangers. Albeit, instead of brick walls for protection, their "bedroom" was surrounded by a metal cage. "We didn't expect that your house would have a mold problem too, especially being the newest one," Starla remarked, looking surprised as she spoke during breakfast one morning. "It's becoming difficult for us to sleep in the spare bedroom now."

The once-neat porch of the Dumans' Congo home became a haphazard mess. Woven mats were hung around the metal cage to afford Nathan and Starla a little privacy. Clothes were draped across the bed and between the metal bars to dry. Abigail stumbled over Daniel's toys by day and took deep breaths of surrender by night, feeling overwhelmed by the transformation their house had endured. While she submitted the front porch to the Lord, she realized that Nathan and Starla had the real trial. Displaced from their own home and with a busy toddler, they were compelled to live in what was essentially a cage to escape the ever-present mold.

With the lull in well-drilling and other campus projects, Keith suggested that Christopher finally replace the mahogany Congolese door with an American-made one in storage. While the American version looked much less intriguing for an entry, it did appear sturdier and more lizard- and rodent-proof.

"If you want that new door to be solid and installed correctly, you'll need to take bricks out around the entryway and use cement and wood to support it," Nathan remarked as Christopher surveyed the empty door space.

"Yes," he answered slowly, reluctantly, allowing his dusty hands to fall at his sides. "I'm guessing you're right."

Although slightly crestfallen that the door project would take several days to complete now, he did not receive any more pressing project assignments to carry him away from this new thorn in his side. In addition to a language-learning center and toddler play area, the outdoor kitchen on the porch now also became a construction zone. As Christopher worked on his house door during the day, Nathan worked on his own house, making progress as new flooring was laid in the living room.

The first several weeks after the heavy downpour was a somewhat trying time for all of the families. Alvina spent her nights on the floor of the spare storage room under a tent of netting to keep out the relentless mosquitoes. Although Alvina never complained, Starla confided another problem to

Abigail one morning. "Alvina's lungs are bothered by the smoldering pile of burned garbage from the yard outside of her window. Could it be burned somewhere else?"

"We can manage that," Abigail agreed, nodding.

As Abigail stirred a batch of pancakes by the warm oven in the outdoor kitchen, she watched Alvina's tall, thin figure walking along the campus drive with a notebook in hand. No matter how poor her night's sleep was, Alvina customarily rose early—sometimes before the light of dawn had risen over the jungle treetops. Abigail knew that she was praying for the many names written there—among them, her two sons in the States.

Displaced and disorganized, Nathan and Starla did their best to sift through their things on the porch in preparation for each day, whether it was sunny or stormy. Adding another trial into the mix, a painful boil developed on Nathan's shoulder.

One afternoon, Nathan rounded the corner from the campus road into the yard. He was astride a four-wheeler, and his chest was bare. His button-up shirt was unbuttoned and flying behind him in the breeze like a superman cape.

"Why, you're going to be the talk of the campus!" Starla exclaimed. "What happened with your shirt, honey? You realize that you're being very culturally immodest, right?"

"This spot on my shoulder especially bothers me when clothing is touching it," Nathan explained, shooting her a sheepish grin.

"Did you have Allen or Jessica look at it?"

"Yes," Nathan stepped off of the four-wheeler. "And they think it's contagious."

Starla's face fell. "I saw a red spot on Daniel's back today that looked pretty similar, but I hoped that it was just a bad bug bite. I'll instruct Mamma Rebecca to wash all of our bedding and clothes in boiling water."

Mamma Rebecca stood nearby and listened to the jumble of English words coming from Starla's mouth. Again, they were clearly articulated but meaningless without clues from her helpful gestures as the missionary pointed to the fire pit and a laundry basket.

Still feeling unsure, the Congolese turned to Abigail questioningly from her position on the porch.

"Clean—hot water," Abigail struggled to remember the right Swahili words. "Very hot water. Wash."

Rebecca's face brightened as she nodded. In a few minutes, she stood over a charcoal burner of glowing coals. She set a pan of water over the heat and lugged a laundry basket of Nathan's clothing over to it.

Abigail's face shone with satisfaction. *Mamma Rebecca understood me! I know that I have reached a breakthrough in my language learning.* Now she felt even more encouraged to venture out and make mistakes. *Give me a few weeks, and I'll be speaking even more,* she joyously thought as she hopped through the broken-down doorway under construction.

In the coming days, as the dampness on the floors evaporated and the mold on the walls multiplied, Nathan's clothes were again and again given the hot-water treatment. And Mamma Rebecca and Abigail became closer friends. Sometimes, when Nathan and Starla carried Daniel over to the Mosier home for lunch, Abigail stayed behind and shared her pan of food with Mamma Rebecca.

Christopher finally completed the installation of the American door to the house. "I don't have a key for the door to unlock it from the outside," he admitted as he tucked his tools into a far corner of the house for safe-keeping. "And I have no idea where one would be."

"Most of the time, we are locking the door from the inside of the house at night," Abigail observed. "It should be just fine."

Although the inconvenience of their displacement was felt by both families, Abigail enjoyed the Rittenours' company and felt greater security in their presence. Instead of walking back after a supper of popcorn and smoothie at the happy Mosier home to enter their dark, lonely one, the sound of Daniel's laughter and Alvina's quiet singing echoed within the brick walls. A light shone on the porch. The outdoor kitchen was piled with food scraps and dishes, but hearts and bellies were full. In spite of the little trials, there remained so much to be thankful for. On many evenings, Nathan or Alvina made a smoothie from frozen bananas, papaya, guava, and pumpkin seeds before sitting in the living area and talking.

"I hope the seeds are blended smoothly enough," Alvina handed Abigail a cup on one such evening. "They are good for treating parasites, you know. That's why I add them in."

All of the adults enjoyed listening to Nathan's stories as they conversed in the cool of the dark evening. Abigail leaned back and closed her eyes, losing herself in one of his tales:

Congo became an unsafe area for foreign missionaries during its long years of war. When the early 2000s ushered in a time of relative peace, a trickling of gospel workers entered the country. Among these few was a small group of Seventh-day Adventists who wanted to see the north-eastern city of Kisangani reached with the three angels' messages: The joyful Mosiers, dedicated Rittenours, and noble Pastor Mtenzi. God accomplished so much through their willing hands and hearts.

Bullet holes still scarred buildings in town when Congo Frontline Mission was launched. Vehicles were a rarity on the dusty roads. And, as the countryside recovered from the terror of war, a spiritual battle continued to wage. With this knowledge, the small mission team organized an evangelistic series in Kisangani. But little did God's workers realize that He had already gone before them to ripen hearts for the hearing of His Word.

In preparation for the series, the mission assigned a Bible worker to cover areas of Kisangani with a personal invitation to the event.

"*Hodi* [Hello, may I enter?]," the Bible worker called out as he walked into a yard of red, packed dirt. He waited for the expected response of "*Karibu*" to assure him that he was welcome.

Suddenly, he heard a commotion behind the mud-brick home. A father with a girl—maybe about twelve years old—rounded a corner of the house in clear distress. The father's hand shook with agitation as he chastised her vehemently.

"What is going on here?" the Bible worker questioned.

The father paused, fear and anger written across his haggard face. He gripped his daughter's shoulder with a viselike hold and said with a tremble in his voice, "The child is a witch."

The young girl choked out a few words to explain, but her crying made it impossible for either adult to understand what she said.

"We should let her explain herself," the Adventist urged the man.

The young girl took a deep breath. "I *was* a witch," she said brokenly, "but I'm not anymore."

As the two men listened, she freely shared the details of her story.

To her family, the girl was an average, hardworking child. But she kept a dark secret from her parents and others in their social circle: she had been initiated into the dark world of witchcraft.

Often on weeknights as the city hushed and families slumbered, she slid from her sleeping mat and slipped into the open night air. Swatting at malaria-carrying mosquitoes, she carefully made her way to the town's burial place—a plot of land somewhat removed from the populous portions of Kisangani.

The young girl was not alone. Other slim figures—appearing more like shadows than human flesh and blood—journeyed from their homes to the graveyard meadow in the starlight. There in the burial place, the child witches met with demonic spirits who captured their rapt attention with exhibitions of magical abilities. They promised the children an array of alluring, mysterious, and irresistible powers over people and events. Their students were spellbound.

TRIALS

Because their parents were terrified of witches, the young people were very careful to conceal their activities. They risked severe discipline from their families if word leaked into the town of their nightly visits. Witchcraft, although not uncommon, held the locals under an oppressive cloud of foreboding. For those who do not know God's stronger power, the work of Satan is fearful.

For weeks, even months, the training sessions in the graveyard continued. And then, one night in the graveyard, everything changed. Instead of meeting their demonic instructors, heavenly angels arrived on the scene.

A flash of light enveloped the group of child witches, thrilling their young hearts with excitement and fear. As their eyes squinted and hearts pounded, they saw angels of a different sort than they had ever seen before. Their presence felt pure and holy, and their light was more glorious than the sun.

The children fell back in astonishment.

One of the angels spoke. "What are you doing here?"

A sudden silence fell over them all.

The angel continued, "You do not have time for this. Jesus is coming soon."

The brilliant light and holy beings disappeared, leaving a group of subdued children who decided to change their allegiance from Satan to Jesus that night.

"What can we do to share this wonderful message with the people in our city?" the young girl questioned.

"Let's go to the churches and tell them," another suggested.

Several months later, a child stood in every church in the city, preaching the Second Advent message to those who had never heard it before.

When the young girl's father and the Adventist Bible worker heard her simple account of what had happened, they were astonished. The Adventist reached into his pocket and pulled out an invitation to the upcoming evangelistic series. "Please come to these meetings if you would like to learn about Jesus and His soon return," he urged.

Both the girl and her family attended the series. She listened to the same message that the angels had spoken—the urgent warning that Jesus would indeed return soon—and her heart was filled with joy. At the close of the series, her entire family was baptized into the Seventh-day Adventist Church along with many others who now believed in Jesus too.

In time, the family moved to Kinshasa, the capital city of Congo, where they lost contact with the missionaries.

ANGELS OVER KISANGANI

In the cool of the evening, as two missionary families gathered around the humble living room and the story was retold, a light still shone in Nathan Rittenour's eyes. The story seemed to fill him with continual faith and hope in God's presence as his family and the others carried on the mission—one that angels had begun.

Abigail smiled in the dim light from a light bulb attached to the ceiling. Crickets chirped on the lawn outside. *God's angels visit Kisangani; in fact, they were here before we ever set foot on this soil.* That assurance filled her heart with peace.

Top: Christopher and Abigail standing at the Congo River's edge.

Right: Abigail pauses for a picture beside the little girl she met at the Kisangani church (mentioned in chapter 5).

Bottom: Well-drilling effort at the mission school. *Left to right*: Christopher, Nathan, and Joel.

Above: Elder Tembo preaches in the chapel with Keith Mosier translating.

Left: Nathan discusses conditions for well drilling with the church planter in Isangi.

Right: The Fuso, stuck on the road between campus and Kisangani.

Below: A Sabbath School teacher uses a newly printed lesson guide for his class.

Above: Starla, Daniel, Mamma Rebecca, and a non-Adventist worker standing on the Dumans' porch.

Left: Shiloh Mosier beside the vehicle where her family narrowly escaped from the mob. (Dents from fists were visible.)

Below: Nathan and Kayumba crossing the Congo by dugout, returning from Isangi.

Left: Christopher and Kayumba pause for a photo on the porch of the walled hotel.

Middle: Children belonging to Congolese workers on campus.

Bottom: Barry Mosier stands by the mission school's sign.

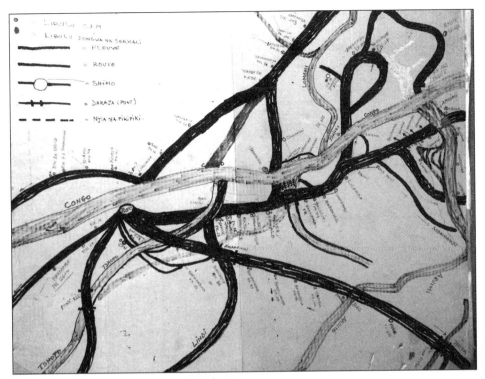

Top: Hand-drawn map of roads, rivers, and church plants.

Left: Road work, a day before the accident.

Bottom left: The Dumans' brick house (photo taken after the accident).

Below: Christopher and Abigail Duman.

CHAPTER 11

PRAYER IS MORE POWERFUL THAN POISON

Caleb Mosier raced around the corner of his family's whitewashed home, breathing heavily as he grinned from ear to ear. "Shiloh is chasing Eleze," he gasped to his mother as she folded stiff pieces of air-dried laundry on the living room sofa. "Isn't it funny?"

Christopher and Abigail approached the Mosier home just in time to hear shrieks of laughter and desperate hollering coming from the direction of the Mosier garden. They could easily see the spot from the rise where the house stood. There in the garden, Shiloh Mosier had cornered the family's young gardener against a stand of banana trees.

"No, no—get it away from me," the smooth-faced young gardener urged with a wild gesture.

"No?" Shiloh said in musical tones. "Why, froggy is your friend." Shiloh mischievously danced on one foot and pushed the wriggling frog in her hands in his direction.

"No," Eleze shook his head vigorously and jumped behind a banana tree stalk.

Shiloh leaped forward. "Yes."

"No!"

"Shiloh Danielle Mosier!" Tammy's voice called from the porch with a tone of authority.

At the sound of her mother's voice, the six-year-old visibly deflated and began a slow ascent up the hill to the porch. Eleze appeared relieved as he nodded appreciatively to Tammy and then scurried to the far corner of the garden plot.

"Shiloh," Tammy reasoned when her eldest daughter finished her slow trudge up the hill. "You know that Eleze does not like frogs. It's actually more than just not liking them—for some people—it's a superstition."

"But Mamma, it seems so silly."

"Be nice to Eleze, Shiloh."

"Yes, Mamma."

Tammy turned to hide her amusement just as the Dumans approached the front steps. "Your oldest seems far advanced for her years," Abigail remarked.

Tammy nodded, ushering the two into the house. "In more ways than one. The other day when Mamma Nikke braided Shiloh's hair, I overheard their conversation. Shiloh launched into a Bible study and recited text after text. I think Mamma Nikke was impressed."

"How special," Abigail replied, smiling. "She's a little missionary."

"She really wants to be." Tammy looked up from her mountain of laundry on the couch nearby as she was struck with an unrelated thought. "Abigail, I didn't realize that when we visited you the other day, Caleb pulled the Tonka truck out of your house and left it in the yard."

"I found it on the porch that night when I finished in the printing container," her friend assured her.

Tammy looked relieved. "The night guard must have returned it to the porch. A toy truck like that could have easily been stolen, you know. I'm so proud of the guard for not stealing it."

"It's wonderful to see God's Spirit working on hearts," Abigail agreed. "He transcends culture and habits to mold us into His image."

The following day, Abigail was reminded once again of God's power to preserve His people in right-doing. The week of prayer was drawing to a close. Sabbath morning sunshine bathed the world with warmth as the Dumans took their favorite shortcut to the chapel where Pastor Mtenzi was scheduled to speak.

Desks and benches were quickly filling up in the large room. The Mosier family sat on a row near the front, dressed in matching-patterned outfits made from local material. Alvina paused by the entry door, unbuckling Daniel from his stroller. Nathan and Starla were not far behind, picking their way across large clumps of grass on the same shortcut Christopher and Abigail had taken.

"I'd like to tell you a story," Mtenzi began the divine message simply. "A story that took place when I worked with a team of evangelists in the bush of Tanzania." The story went like this:

A younger Pastor Mtenzi conversed quietly with a fellow Bible worker. "Well," his friend sighed. "Should we return to the city? This village in the bush is obviously resistant to hearing the truth."

The meeting tent nearby had the capacity to hold many interested listeners, but only a few curious locals meandered out of the village to hear God's Word.

"I know that it feels discouraging," broad-shouldered Mtenzi replied, turning to his friend. "But I feel strongly that God led us here to begin this work and that we should do our part to complete it. Success or failure, the results are up to Him."

The team of Bible workers encouraged each other to press on in spite of an apparent lack of interest from the village. Several days later, things began to look up: they received an invitation to a home-cooked meal in the village. Every face in the group brightened upon hearing the news.

"I would love a break from eating cassava and beans every day," one of the men said, grinning. While continuing the evangelism effort, they counted down the days to the dinner. Maybe this invitation was part of God's plan, they thought, a plan that would make a breakthrough in this difficult village.

Then a new element of the invitation reached their ears. "The leaders have consulted together to plan you harm," a trustworthy contact from the village warned them. "They have made a townswoman invite you, and she will poison the food that you are expected to eat. Don't go and eat from her table!"

Mtenzi straightened as he listened. "We will go anyway," he said calmly to the wide-eyed messenger.

When the time came, the evangelists were welcomed into the house warmly and beckoned to a table laden with steaming pots of food.

The men sat down, but before taking a bite, the Adventists politely motioned to the cook.

"You prepared this wonderful meal for us; thus, you should be the first to eat it."

She swallowed. "Oh, oh, no, no." She shook her head a little too vigorously. "You go first."

"How do we know that there is no poison in the food?" Mtenzi asked.

For a moment, no one spoke a word. The member of their group most inclined to abandon their mission and turn back seemed to hesitate. But then, gingerly, the man reached for a small piece of food and quickly ate it.

The men waited. In minutes, the man who had taken from the dish began to exhibit obvious signs of poisoning.

"There *is* poison in the food," Mtenzi asserted, then turned to the hostess. "Why did you do this?"

No longer able to pretend innocence, the woman bowed her head. "The leaders of the town made me poison the food," she confessed. Then her eyes brightened with a challenge. "But I do have an idea. I will ask the God that you serve that He will remove the poison from the food so it will not harm you. Then we will see how real He is."

The men around the table exchanged glances. Recognizing this as a challenge to God's power and a test of their faith, they claimed the promises of His Word.

Every head bowed as their cook began to pray. The men prayed with her in their hearts, asking that their heavenly Father would use this poisoning attempt for His glory. When the praying ended, each faithful man dipped his spoon into the dish and ate the poisoned food.

"We finished the entire meal, leaving no scraps behind," Mtenzi recalled to the listeners in the quaint chapel on campus. Abigail noted a twinkle in his dark eyes. "And the poison meant to sicken or kill us had no effect. We waited for the poison to harm us, but we felt fine." He laughed quietly, deeply. "It has been years now, and we are still waiting for that poison to kill us."

As news spread around the village that the carefully planned poison could not sicken God's messengers, people flocked to the evangelistic tent. The meetings continued with greater fervor, and empty chairs were few. People long confined to the darkness of superstition, fear, and witchcraft saw a great light. They wanted to hear about the God in heaven who made poison of no effect and who gave His messengers the fearlessness and courage to persevere and pray in the face of great odds. The evangelistic series in the bush ended with decisions for Christ and baptisms.

As Abigail reflected on Pastor Mtenzi's story, she was again reminded of God's power to work through less-than-ideal circumstances. *Even poison was used to bring souls to the cross*, she marveled. Out of the adventures, events, and trials she had experienced in the past several months now, a common theme was developing in her mind. God's protection from the rock-throwing beggar and over the Congo River in a crowded dugout to Isangi. His presence through her personal struggle with the threat of robbers in the night and other dangers. Stories of miraculous angel visitations and intervention on behalf of the Lord's servants. Combining all the events together gave Abigail an overwhelming sense of peace. Over and over again, God's power dwarfed all the foes of darkness. "I am one of His servants," she whispered. "And come what may, I will choose to trust Him."

CHAPTER 12

A WARNING

Finally, the day of the long-anticipated arrival of Barry Mosier was here. The Mosier children were energetic, rehearsing with glee their excitement about the many stories their grandfather would read to them. And the missionaries all wondered what a reaction to Alvina's garlic-lemongrass tea would look like on his gentle face.

Barry Mosier was a quiet man, with short salt-and-pepper hair, glasses, and a particularly composed and calm manner. In fact, the trip to Africa with its accompanying exhaustion and extreme jet lag seemed to have little effect on the seasoned missionary. The morning after his arrival, he stewed over a list of agenda items he wanted to accomplish during the intervals between reading storybooks with his grandchildren.

One item included on his list was viewing a 3ABN interview featuring Keith and himself recorded earlier that year in August. On one of Barry's first evenings on campus, the missionary families gathered together in the Mosiers' warm living room. Keith propped his laptop on a chair. After several minutes of straining to hear the recorded conversation over the playful banter of Shiloh and Anna, he connected two small speakers.

"I am looking forward to watching this interview," Pastor Mtenzi said in his deep voice as he settled on the couch.

Keith smiled and nodded as he took a seat. "We missed including you in the interview, Pastor Mtenzi, and wish that you could have been in America with us."

"Ah," the Tanzanian nodded. "I will join you next time, Lord willing."

The interview included an account of Congo Frontline Missions' history, and as soon as the video recording ended, a discussion of those early events ensued.

"When we first decided to come to Congo, many encouraged us not to." Tammy placed a jar of honey on the kitchen table, where she monitored her children's play. "When the mission was first established, there were no roads to reach Kisangani. Even a vehicle for the mission had to be flown in."

A WARNING

"My wife and children and I left Tanzania a few weeks before Keith and his family did," Pastor Mtenzi recalled. "People told us, 'Don't go. It is a dangerous place.' And no one seemed interested in coming with us." He paused. "We crossed the border into Congo and found that soldiers with machine guns were everywhere. We found a space on the floor of a building owned by friends, where we fanned our little ones throughout the night in the heat. We had no mosquito nets and risked malaria, but by God's grace, we made it to Kisangani in good health."

"Those beginning days must have been challenging," Abigail said sympathetically as Jessica's almond-shaped brown eyes blinked at the pastor's words.

"It was," the man replied. "But it was all OK," he said simply. "Many people know Jesus now because we were willing to come."

"True," Keith agreed as he pulled little Anna onto his lap and tousled her mop of blond ringlets. "One memory from our earlier days will stay etched in my mind forever. I remember meeting one church planter's wife who lay on her deathbed. She clutched her husband's hand in those final moments and pleaded with him. 'Don't allow anything to stop you from carrying on this work,' she said. She saw how ripe the harvest is."

After setting Anna down, he straightened and reached for his guitar hanging on the wall. His fingers pressed against the strings as he continued. "The darkness of evil is very strong here. Voodoo and spiritualism are deeply rooted in the culture. But a light is shining in Congo and spreading to many people now."

"The harvest truly is great, but the laborers are few," he sang softly as Tammy and Alvina conversed in the kitchen.

Sitting on the couch by Jessica, Abigail felt deeply impressed by the solemnity and importance of the mission. She admired the missionaries whom she worked with. *We need more people who are willing to take risks for the sake of bearing light into the darkness*, she thought.

Another highlight included on Barry Mosier's agenda was a special day when the mission school beside the road would welcome him as its namesake. Mamma Rose's face shone from more than just the scrub she had given it that morning. She tied her baby onto her back, stepped away from the lines of waiting students, and began to call out instructions.

"Today, we are going to welcome Barry Mosier, Keith Mosier's daddy, to our school," Mama Rose announced. "Our school is named for this great man. We must make him proud today."

By the time Christopher drove Abigail over to the schoolhouse on a four-wheeler, the young people had decorated the yard beautifully. The humble dirt walkway was festooned with palm branches shoved into the tan earth and bent to make bowers of living green. The school children lovingly wove red hibiscus and other jungle flowers into the fluttering palm leaves.

The children lined up to prepare for the arrival of the school's namesake. There were close to sixty students, and Abigail smiled in recognition as she spotted little faces belonging to the Adventists on campus. The rest of the children were from Huit. Mamma Rose walked from Huit each day to serve as a teacher.

When Pastor Mtenzi's 4-Runner pulled into the schoolyard, the eagerness of the throng reached a high pitch. Children waved their woven palm fronds and jungle flowers high in the air, chanting that Barry Mosier had come to Kisangani. They thanked him and called him their daddy.

"This is a welcome that would warm anyone's heart," Abigail remarked to Chris at her side.

Barry stepped out of the passenger seat of Mtenzi's vehicle and marched to the schoolhouse, surrounded by the throng of children. He graciously listened to a carefully written report by the headmaster, which followed the welcome. "We want to thank you so much for this school and would like to ask for rain jackets and boots for the teachers, who must walk through the rain and mud on the road on some days."

"I am so glad that you not only want to receive an education but also, most importantly, want to learn about Jesus," Barry said to the squirming Congolese children who responded with gusto.

I wish that the people who donated the money for this school could be here today, Abigail thought. *If they could only stand here and behold the fruit of stepping out in faith to give.*

The Mosiers, who were also present to watch the festivities, along with the Dumans, returned to campus in high spirits.

During that same week, Nathan and Abigail continued the printing work in earnest. As the cucumber plants in her garden plot flourished, Abigail labored in the air conditioning of the container not far away, watching sheet after sheet of clean white paper being peppered with the words of life.

"We are printing Spirit of Prophecy books that have never before been printed here." Nathan looked excited as he shared with Barry on the following Sabbath afternoon. "Abigail has been assisting with the printing jobs while I oversee the installation of new floors in our house."

"I heard about the mold," Barry replied, nodding, and then took a deep breath. "And it's wonderful to hear about your progress with the books. God is doing great things. Although I might add . . ." his voice trailed off.

Abigail looked up expectantly from a book little Talitha had shoved into her lap.

A WARNING

Barry continued, "I remember the breakthroughs that my family and mission team made while working in Tanzania. Every time something like this happens, especially when it has to do with publishing the Spirit of Prophecy, I have seen the devil unleash all of his fury."

Abigail felt a tiny shiver travel down her spine as she listened to Barry's words. Everything on campus seemed so peaceful. Birds chattered in the treetops outside the Mosiers' home, and little blond-headed children babbled on the porch and stroked their gentle dog, Simba. Abigail thought of the trials that had come to Nathan and his family with the stress of Daniel's lungs and their mold issues. *Are the Rittenours' trials a result of our progress in the container? Or have we yet to experience the real unleashing of the devil's fury?*

As he often did, Keith pulled his guitar from the wall and brushed across the smooth wooden front with his hand. He ran his fingers over the strings expertly, following the tune of a lively children's song. Shiloh, Caleb, and Anna leaped across the blue mat in the living room in time to the music. Allen and Jessica conversed nearby with Pastor Mtenzi, expressing their thankfulness that Elder Tembo and his wife had been able to visit for the week of prayer and had safely arrived in Tanzania once again. Alvina slipped into a side room to talk with her two sons in the States, while Tammy changed Talitha's banana smoothie–smeared dress shirt.

Christopher sank back into a chair and watched the satisfyingly peaceful afternoon unfold. Nathan and Starla brought little Daniel back to the familiar brick house in the clearing for a nap in their front porch bedroom. Somewhere on campus, Mamma Rebecca was taking the Sabbath easy while Kayumba cradled a child in his arms as he sat on his concrete steps, and Esther stirred a pot of beans.

Putting Barry's words out of her mind, Abigail enjoyed the quietness all across the campus that evening. *All is well in our little world.*

CHAPTER 13

POPCORN ON THE BLUFF

Don't worry, Shiloh, we won't forget to pick up Mr. Allen and Miss Jessica from their clinic house," Keith said reassuringly as Shiloh expressed her concerns. The box cruiser bumped across the campus in the direction of the palm tree circle and string of brick homes. It was another bright Sabbath morning. Ever since the heavy downpour that jump-started the mold in the Dumans' house, it had rained every few days. Unfortunately, the mild breaks from the rain allowed the roads to only partially dry just in time for another downpour.

Christopher and Abigail steadied themselves on the back benches of the vehicle, holding on to their water bottles and Bibles, as the Smiths joined them.

"I want to sit next to Miss Abby," Anna suddenly chirped.

Tammy craned her neck around from the front seat as Keith eased the box cruiser over a pothole. "Is that OK?"

Abigail nodded with a smile.

"Alright, Anna, stay close to Abby and let her keep you steady on this next stretch of road."

Abigail slipped her arm around the little girl as they bumped and jostled down the road to Kisangani. At some points on the trek, the road narrowed to such an extreme that locals on foot were forced to press into the creeping jungle to make room. Walled ruts of drying mud lined the way on both sides—sometimes up to two feet high. The box cruiser's wheels bounced and spun as Keith continued on.

Nathan and Starla—the latter clutching Daniel in a death-grip—carefully followed behind them. Proper car seats and infant seating were not available for purchase in this third-world country.

"We need to fix this road," Allen whined, rubbing his head after a particularly solid bump where his head hit the vehicle roof.

"Whenever we have a long enough break in the rain," Christopher responded.

POPCORN ON THE BLUFF

The Adventist church they would visit today was new to the Dumans and not far from the banks of the mighty Congo River. Keith pulled onto a winding dirt path and then parked on a flat, sandy spot at the base of several mango trees. Their jagged, gnarly roots protruding from the sandy soil served as perfect seats for fishermen who were mending their nets while they chatted.

The missionary group walked single file down a winding path, skirting between houses and clumps of tall grasses until the familiar sound of singing greeted their ears.

When the local church members spotted their American visitors, they scrambled for every available plastic chair that could be found in the nearby homes. The usual crowd of raggedly dressed children from the village stood nearby. They gaped as the church family lovingly stretched out their hands to welcome the honored guests.

"Some Congolese have never seen people with pale skin in person before," Tammy explained. "That's why we so often receive a lot of stares."

While an adult Sabbath School class began in the sanctuary, the families joined a children's Sabbath School on the other side of the brick walls. Through the open windows came snippets of Swahili and Lingala between the children's songs. When the clapping and singing came to an end, the benches on the grass were completely full of little children. They watched as a teacher leafed through a booklet in his hand.

Abigail's eyes squinted at the familiar type on the cover. *I printed this book*, she realized. *This is the children's Sabbath School lesson booklet that Nathan and I have been working on.*

When Tammy realized that children's Sabbath School teachers had no program materials to guide them through classes, she and a previous visitor from the United States composed a booklet with weekly lessons for the younger generation. When it was completed, Keith saw that the pages were translated into Swahili and then handed the project over to Nathan.

Seeing the book in the hands of the teacher warmed Abigail's heart. It had made quite a journey through the mechanical works of the printer to her hands where it was folded and stapled and then finally in the grasp of this man. She recognized the value of each step in the journey. When it came time for the songs, a woman dressed in her Sabbath best stepped forward with another familiar work—a songbook also printed in the humble container on campus. What joy!

When the class had ended, the missionaries made their way into the church. Seats had been thoughtfully left empty for them at the front—always the best they had to offer, of course—while the locals and children sat on benches behind them.

During the service, Allen Smith shared his testimony as Keith translated. "I was born to missionary parents," the young doctor began. "And my dad was a pilot. As a young boy, I wanted to be a missionary too. Now, it is our dream to bring good health care to the Congolese people who need it."

Many in the audience nodded approvingly. Word had already spread that the man and his young wife had come to offer medical help to the people around Kisangani.

When Allen had finished, Keith highlighted his own journey—his call to Congo and then how God called Nathan and Starla, Alvina, Allen, and Jessica, and finally Christopher and Abigail to the Democratic Republic of Congo's tropical forests. He summed up their mission and commitment to seeing it through for however long God provided.

"We are so glad to see that each family is here today," Keith smiled with palpable warmth in his voice.

The closing hymn swelled in beautiful harmony. After the first few notes, Abigail recognized the song: "Take the Name of Jesus With You." *This has become my theme song for these dear people*, she thought in her heart. *So many of them are truly children of "sorrow and woe." How I wish that each and every Congolese would find comfort in Christ's name.* "Precious name, O how sweet! Hope of earth and joy of heaven."

The sense of family and belonging to a people she barely knew struck her with sudden tearfulness. *Thank You for the miracle of Your love*, she prayed in amazement. *It unites us as a family.*

Before the group loaded into the vehicles again, Allen stopped to chat with the fishermen under the mango trees. The men were dressed in simple, drab attire, and their attitudes were just as unpretentious as they expertly sorted through their nets for any new holes. They grinned when Allen approached and seemed flattered that someone took an interest in their way of life.

"Yes, we have seen crocodiles in this river as long as fifteen feet," one man said, gesturing. "They fear us, though," he boasted. "We shoot every time we see one."

Before they returned home for a shared meal, Keith had another objective in mind. He found a suitable area to park beside the road and watched as Nathan pulled in behind him. Tammy reached into the recesses of the vehicle and pulled out several bags of popcorn and cookies. "We have some snacks to tide us over until we reach campus," she said cheerily.

After unloading occupants and snacks, the men jumped from the vehicles and led the women and children up a mild incline to a flat rise on the banks of the Congo River. Just as rapidly as the group of missionaries gathered on the bluff, a group of onlookers surrounded them. Abigail noticed that most of them were children and young men.

POPCORN ON THE BLUFF

The cliff jutted abruptly downward and was covered with grasses, scraggly roots, and tangled shrubbery. The Congo River stretched far and wide until it finally disappeared into forested land that appeared impenetrable, dense, and endless. A strip of jungle lay at the center of the river, surrounded by rapids on either side. Several naked boys swam in the frothy waters below the cliff, pushing against the current with their wiry legs.

"I'm going to take a canoe out on this river one of these days," Allen asserted as he dug deep into his popcorn bag and crunched heartily.

"You'll have to find someone else to go with you," Jessica half-teased.

"Oh, you'll go with me," he replied. "I know you will."

"Down there with the crocodiles," Abigail added with a smile, secretly hoping that Allen would leave Christopher out of the expedition.

Keith stood a slight distance away, engaging several young men in conversation, while Barry remained nearby and breathed a few cautionary words. "Be sure not to take any photos of the river," he warned. "In this Congo postwar climate, a lot of people remain suspicious. At a different site along the river where boats were docking and being unloaded, someone spotted one of us missionaries taking a picture." Barry reached for a cookie from a woven bag. "Long story short, that picture cost us sixty dollars, and the local church planter was put in jail."

Abigail gasped. "Why?"

"The church planter was associated with us. Here in Congo, everything is connected. When one person gets in trouble, others can automatically be in danger, too—even if they are perfectly innocent and unaware. We got the church planter out of jail, and everything was sorted out in the long run because authorities realized that we were not spies, but now we know better than to take photos of the river. It's too risky. Initial reactions in this culture are strong."

Christopher listened as he leaned against the side of the vehicle with a bag of popcorn in his hand, digging into the bag every few moments for another fistful of the fluffy snack.

Suddenly, a young man rushed recklessly toward the group on the bluff. The watchful throng parted like the biblical Red Sea. Running up to plant himself squarely in front of Chris, he extended his hand with an open palm.

"Meeester, give me!" he demanded.

Christopher paused for a few quiet moments. No one said a word, unsure what to do. All eyes were on Chris. If he gave popcorn to this man, wouldn't all the others want popcorn too? The missionaries didn't have treats for all. Would the people grow angry?

Popcorn is available at the market in town, and it is not a novelty item here,

93

Chris's wife considered briefly. *Hasn't this man had popcorn before? What is he trying to prove?*

Chris hesitated only for a moment. He reached into his bag and gave the man a handful.

The Congolese brought his fist to his mouth and then abruptly turned on his heels. He rushed back through the crowd with his "trophy."

Had it been a dare? Christopher shook his head in uncertainty. "I feel so relieved," Abigail said, tucking her small hand beneath his arm. "I feel sure that you did the right thing under the circumstances, but for a few moments, I wasn't sure what *was* the right thing to do!"

Chris laughed a little and shifted his stance. He was relieved too.

"Safe, safe?" Daniel, who had been standing by Nathan's pant leg, suddenly ran to Starla nearby. Young as he was, he seemed to sense a change in the emotional climate among the adults on the cliff.

"Yes, you're safe," Starla scooped the little boy up.

"You know," Abigail observed, "If these locals wanted to, they could so easily push us off this little ridge into the river below." Having voiced the sudden thought, she quickly decided that she didn't like it. What made the difference between the mutual love she felt among church family and the hint of distrust in her heart for the Congolese on the bluff? *God's love unites His children*, she thought. *I suppose that my only fear is the anger of those who do not know or love Him.*

Realizing that she would never have a picture of the river view below to carry with her, Abigail tried to capture the scene from the overlook in her mind. The missionaries enjoyed the cool wind gliding up from the shining waters below for a few minutes longer. The breeze felt like air conditioning in the heat of the day.

CHAPTER 14

THIN ICE

"Esther, Kayumba's wife, needs to be taken across town today," Christopher announced as he returned to the porch on Sunday morning. Abigail was washing dishes at the outdoor sink. Christopher continued, "I just heard that her grandfather recently died."

True to the report Chris had received, Kayumba soon stopped by the house to borrow a motorcycle that Christopher stored on the porch some nights. The Congolese planned to take Esther down the long, winding road to the motorcycle washing pond at Kisangani. From there, she would be near enough to town to catch a moto-taxi.

An hour later, Kayumba returned the motorcycle. A concerned expression was on his face as he parked in the grass. Nathan looked over at the faithful Congolese worker. He was about to take Daniel for a walk in the stroller but stopped when he noticed Kayumba's changed demeanor.

"What is the news of the day?" he asked—the usual greeting of the Congolese.

"*Nzuri*," Kayumba swung a leg over the side of the motorbike, delivering the expected reply. No matter how bad a Congolese's day had been, "*nzuri*," or "good," was nearly always the response. Then, without comment, Kayumba reached into his worn pants pocket and produced a wrinkled piece of paper. "Look at this."

Nathan frowned as he scanned the printed words.

"Someone mass-printed these pamphlets in town," Kayumba explained, his hands hanging awkwardly at his sides. "This pamphlet announces that a protest will be held against the president of Congo."

The current president of the country was long overdue to step down from his position, but for many years he had found excuses to remain in office. The Congolese were growing tired of feeling that they had no choice in the matter. The unsettled winter season was fast approaching.

"Do you have any advice for us?" Nathan asked quickly. "Starla and I were planning to take a trip into Kisangani tomorrow."

"The protest is planned for tomorrow," Kayumba spoke solemnly. "All of the major businesses will be closed, and there will be little if any transportation on the streets. I heard that you planned to make the trip into town tomorrow, and I wanted to warn you: don't go."

Nathan nodded. "Thank you, Kayumba."

The Congolese nodded as he turned and left.

As the Americans continued to familiarize themselves with the culture of the area, Kayumba's friendship had proved invaluable to their mission. During previous seasons of political instability, his connections (he belonged to a well-known, popular tribe) and familiarity with Kisangani alerted him to helpful information time and again.

The next morning dawned with a strange urgency awakening in Abigail's chest. She found it difficult to describe her growing premonition. While Monday's early hours were still cool, she picked up a hoe and trudged over to the garden plot across from the Rittenour's empty house. Starla's familiar figure was already bent over her plants. Carefully, she fertilized each one using a metal spoon and a stick.

"Kayumba picked up this fertilizer for us in Kisangani, and I think it will do wonders for our plants," Starla remarked as Abigail donned her sun hat. "I brought an extra spoon out so you can feed your green beans and cucumbers if you'd like."

"Thank you." Abigail took the spoon and searched for a stick to poke a little hole in the loose earth at the base of each plant.

The minutes ticked by. As the rising sun sent humid waves of heat over the unshaded area, she could feel the sweat beads on her brow. "I don't have long to work in the garden this morning," she finally announced to her friend. "I really need to work in the printing container."

"At least finish fertilizing your row of beans," Starla insisted. "You're going to see such a difference in the health of the plants."

Abigail sighed softly and continued for a few more minutes. Finally, she set the hoe down. "I must go to the container."

Though Starla seemed mildly disapproving of her, Abigail couldn't stifle her sense of urgency any longer. It impelled her across the driveway to the container, where she quickly started up the generator and then began a new print job. The young missionary gazed at the newly stapled book in her hands—*The Story of Redemption.*

Did she feel this urgency because of Barry's warning from the previous week? Or was it because she had seen the books being used by local laypeople in the church? Abigail could not say for sure, but as the hours passed, Barry's words continued to echo in her mind: *The devil is unhappy. Expect opposition.*

In a place gripped by such spiritual darkness, surely the devil would not give up without a struggle. "I'm going to do my part to see God's work accomplished." Abigail gritted her teeth and worked with a greater determination.

"Are you heading over to the container again?" Chris asked during lunch as Abigail set a small stack of tin plates in the sink for washing.

"Yes," she said as she quickly rinsed each one. "The printer is actually running through my lunch break today. Nathan doesn't like to leave it operating for long periods without someone to watch for glitches, so I can't stay here long."

"You seem pretty motivated," he observed, reaching for his hat as he set out for an afternoon project elsewhere on campus.

"I feel that our time is short," Abigail confided quickly. "And I'm not exactly sure why. But no day is promised, and we never know how much time we have left to work."

As she headed toward the container again, a familiar hymn played in her mind, "Work, for the Night Is Coming."

Lost in a stack of booklets, Abigail scarcely looked up when Nathan entered the dimly lit printing area. "The rain has slacked long enough for us to begin work on the road to town." His words broke into her reverie. "I just wanted to check on progress here before I talk to your husband about taking the Bobcat and Fuso truck out on the road."

"The printer is running low on ink," Abigail reported. "Otherwise, the printing process has been running smoothly."

"I'll show you how to refill ink cartridges," he replied.

With the task completed, Abigail was once again left alone in the container, listening to the hum of the printer and the drone of the generator outside. She couldn't help but wonder what would happen in Kisangani today—the day of the scheduled protest. Kisangani had remained relatively peaceful since the great war. Would its people turn to violence to get the attention of political leaders?

Despite a sense of uncertainty in the air, the daily labor on campus continued as normal. Kayumba, Christopher, and Joel listened as Nathan laid out plans for the road work. Barry still balanced his time between mission business and moments on the couch in the Mosier living room surrounded by his towheaded grandkids.

One afternoon, he stopped by the Dumans' house with a clipboard under his arm, seeking to meet with them.

"Today is not the best for us," Abigail explained. "Christopher is away on a project right now."

"It's OK, I'll meet with you both another time," Barry said as he walked away.

On the following day, Abigail walked to the Mosier home in hopes of finding Barry and scheduling their meeting. She wondered what it was all about but tried not to seem too curious.

When Abigail reached the Mosiers' porch, she heard voices through the screened and barred windows of the living room. "Grandpa has to go talk with Pastor Mtenzi now," Tammy explained to her children as they looked up from a picture book.

"Aww, Grandpa," Shiloh begged. "Can't you read one more story?"

"I'll be back in a few hours," Barry answered as he slowly straightened from his comfortable seat just as Abigail gently knocked on the screened door.

"Christopher and I will have time this evening to meet with you if that works," she suggested.

"Oh," the older man ran his fingers through his graying hair. "I have plans for this evening, but could we plan on Thursday morning? Maybe at eight o'clock in the chapel?"

"That sounds fine to me. I'll let Christopher know."

As Barry set off with his laptop in hand and a backpack slung across his shoulder, Alvina took up the empty space on the couch. "Shiloh, why don't we continue reading in *The Great Controversy*? Do you remember where we left off?"

"Yes, I remember, Grandma," the precocious six-year-old articulated.

Although squirming, little Anna lingered nearby as Shiloh and Caleb sat beside their grandmother. Talitha happily occupied herself by removing book after book from a shelf screwed to the wall, while Tammy paused in the kitchen to bid Mamma Nikke a peaceful afternoon.

" 'And all was ready for the fire to be lighted,' " Alvina read aloud as two young faces nearby looked especially solemn. " 'The martyr was once more exhorted to save himself by renouncing his errors. "What errors," said Huss, "shall I renounce? I know myself guilty of none. I call God to witness that all that I have written and preached has been with the view of rescuing souls from sin and perdition; and, therefore, most joyfully will I confirm with my blood that truth which I have written and preached." ' "[1]

Alvina paused to take a breath as Shiloh looked up questioningly. "Grandma," the young girl started, smoothing a crease in her play dress thoughtfully, "are there people today who are martyred like John Huss was?"

"I'm sure there are, Shiloh," the soft-spoken voice replied gently. "But our heavenly Father can give each one strength to be faithful to the end."

Shiloh looked thoughtful as she continued to listen to the account.

As the sunlight of the day receded into the shadows of the jungle, Keith and Tammy leaned against the support beams on their porch and chatted with the Dumans, who had found another purposeful (yet convenient) reason to stop by.

"Did we hear anything from Kayumba about the protest in Kisangani?" Abigail asked eagerly.

"Yes, we did hear news from town," Keith answered. "Kayumba stopped by the office earlier today to let us know that there was no protest after all. The streets remained fairly empty, and people stayed inside their homes. Kayumba said they are afraid that violence will break out."

"That sounds like a good sign," Chris suggested.

"Yes," Keith slipped an arm around Tammy's waist. "Kisangani has generally remained pretty stable. I was hoping that nothing would come of the protest."

"Is there a way of knowing who is behind the attempt to incite political unrest?" Abigail wondered.

Keith shook his head. "There's no telling. It could have been an organization, or it could have been a single person who had the papers printed in some little shop in town."

"I'm just thankful that Kisangani is peaceful." Tammy laughed quickly. "We have so much to be grateful for."

"Speaking of thankfulness, we have made great progress recently on several objectives of the mission." Keith launched into an update regarding a local radio station the mission oversaw, Pastor Mtenzi's evangelistic work, and the ministry budget. Hope shone in his eyes. Always upbeat, the leader constantly walked with a presence of optimistic anticipation.

In the early hours of the next morning, Abigail awoke to a wiggling sensation beneath her pillow. She blinked in the darkness and wondered what had awakened her. Then she realized what it was.

"Chris." Her voice cut through the still air. "I think there's a lizard underneath my pillow."

"Mmmm," he mumbled. "I'm sure it's fine."

Does he know what he's talking about? She drifted back to sleep.

Several hours later, another movement sent her sailing straight up in bed. Wide awake now, she reached for her headlamp and confirmed her suspicions. "Aha! I knew it!"

"What?" Chris slowly blinked in the light, still half-asleep.

"I just felt a lizard crawling underneath me!" she frantically pounded her pillow.

Christopher turned over in bed with a sigh. "Well, we have a long day ahead of us out on the road."

He was right. Kayumba, Joel, and the mission's non-Adventist Congolese driver ambled up to their porch just as Christopher finished the last corn-oat pancake on his plate. The driver was a quiet fellow and made little eye contact as Christopher greeted the small group. The man went by the title Chauffeur and always wore a purple tie-dye shirt.

As Christopher and Nathan joined the group walking up the path to the campus drive, Abigail stood and watched them leave. *May God grant them all safety.*

When passersby saw the crew from campus working on the road, they often smiled and waved. "I'm beginning to feel pretty popular," Chris chuckled later that evening as the couple compared notes about the day. "This will make the lives of the many locals much easier—especially those who travel from their gardens in the jungle to the city."

"Maybe the teachers at the Barry Mosier school will no longer need rain boots," Abigail quipped with a slight smile. "If the water can drain off to the sides of the road, rather than create deep ruts in the middle, the rainy season will be more pleasant for everyone."

"Right," her husband nodded. "Our one hiccup today happened when the Fuso got stuck in the mud. It was at a narrow spot in the road, and the usual group of onlookers gathered with great interest to see how we would get out of our pickle."

"How *did* you pull that big truck out?" she asked.

"Nathan had already returned to campus, so I called him over the radio. He drove the Land Cruiser over, and we were able to pull the Fuso out with it. While we waited for him to arrive, Kayumba and Chauffeur tried their best to dig around the buried wheels with shovels." He shook his head with a wry smile. "I knew it would take something more than a shovel if we expected to get any work done today."

A few moments of silence passed as they listened to laughter from the huts outside, where warm coals glowed from a charcoal burner.

"I've wanted to remind you that we have a meeting with Barry Mosier in the chapel tomorrow morning." Abigail pulled a Swahili dictionary from their bookcase and headed into the bedroom for safety under the mosquito net.

"OK," Christopher agreed as he followed her.

"Do you have any idea why Barry wants to meet with us?" Abigail asked. "We are not a long-term missionary family, even though we receive a stipend for food and other necessities. I sure hope we don't have to keep an active cash-box account on a laptop like Nathan and Keith do. It seems very complicated."

"I guess we'll see."

Just then, the scuffling of Nathan's boots on the porch alerted them to his entry. Alvina had already retired for the night, but the Rittenours were just returning from their own meeting with Barry that afternoon.

"Pray that it doesn't rain tonight, Chris." Nathan's voice sounded concerned as he crossed the living room. "If it rains hard, the hours of work your team accomplished on the road today will be ruined."

Christopher quickly joined him in the dimly lit area. Voices hushed as Starla reminded the men that Daniel had fallen into slumber for the night.

"The weather is out of our hands, but it would sure be nice if it didn't rain," Nathan repeated quietly.

"We'll be praying!" Christopher's voice grew closer as he joined his wife in the bedroom once again.

Before going to sleep, Abigail carefully searched through the bedsheets and under her pillow for lizards. Then, with the light switched off, Nathan led their prayer together as usual.

"Lord, if it is Your will, please keep it from raining so that the road work done today wasn't all for nothing," he prayed. "Please, Father, keep it from raining."

Sometime during the night hours, the gentle pattering of raindrops began to fall on the metal roof. Bushy palm branches scratched across the metal roof in the breeze. Christopher slightly raised his head in the darkness and listened to the sound of the rain. Abigail sensed his stirring. She couldn't understand why God allowed the rain to fall. But maybe it would fit into His overall plans for their ultimate good.

---

1. Ellen G. White, *The Great Controversy Between Christ and Satan* (Mountain View, CA: Pacific Press®, 1950), 109.

CHAPTER 15

THE ACCIDENT

On the morning of November 1, 2017, Abigail gritted her teeth and took a cold early morning shower. Then, while Christopher took his shower, she dressed in a red blouse and jean skirt and settled on a bench in their room to read her Bible. The book of Psalms had been especially comforting to her whenever the threat of robbers came to the forefront of her mind. Morning and evening, the words of the psalmist reminded her to have faith and trust in the Lord no matter what troubles life brought.

"I surrender this day into Your hands," she prayed after closing the cover of her Bible. "Please keep us ever faithful and trusting in Your continued care."

With peace in her heart and a sense of relief that the scheduled political protest in Kisangani hadn't happened, she slipped on a comfortable pair of sandals and shuffled to the outdoor porch. The Rittenours were already awake.

Children's voices traveled on the early morning breeze from the Barry Mosier school, where they repeated Mamma Rose's lessons aloud. An elusive African grey parrot cawed in a nearby treetop.

"We're expected at the meeting in five minutes," Christopher reminded Abigail as she flipped the last pancake over the heat of their gas stove top.

"Don't worry about putting things away—I can take care of the clean-up," Alvina offered as she took Abigail's place at the stove.

The younger woman reached for her favorite blue water bottle with a look of gratitude. "Thank you, Alvina; I appreciate it." The kitchen was a disaster, as usual.

Nathan reigned over his own batch of pancakes on a separate burner as Starla hand-fed Daniel where he perched on a little stool.

"I sure hope we're not in trouble for anything," Abigail remarked as they stepped over large clumps of grass on the shortcut to the campus green. "Why does Barry want to meet with us?"

"Stop worrying about it—I'm sure that everything is just fine," Christopher again insisted. "We'll find out the answer soon enough."

THE ACCIDENT

Mamma Rebecca paused to wave from her pineapple garden as the couple passed by. Soon, she would be walking over to their house to help prepare lunch on the cement porch.

As they reached the chapel, a morning devotional had just ended. The couple watched as campus workers and hired help from the village of Huit streamed out of the open door. Chauffeur's purple tie-dye shirt stood out like a sore thumb in the surrounding group of men while Kayumba and Joel set off in the direction of the parked Fuso truck.

"It looks like the rain won't dampen work efforts on the road to Kisangani after all," Chris observed, sounding hopeful. "I see the crew preparing to leave."

"There are more men here than we have living on campus," his wife noticed.

"Keith is hiring some of the residents of Huit to help with the road."

"Will you join them later?"

"I'm not sure. We'll see what Nathan has planned."

Pastor Mtenzi sat quietly in the chapel with his hands folded over a desk. Keith and Barry quickly shuffled up the center aisle to join him as he and the Dumans waited.

Barry cleared his throat. "Well, we've been wanting to meet with you two because we can see that God is working," he began.

"With Christopher assisting on well drilling and campus maintenance, he and Nathan have completed quite a few projects," Keith plunged ahead. "Some projects I had been hoping to see finished for many months. It has been a relief to see them get done so quickly."

"We also expect Mr. Christopher to speak for an upcoming evangelistic series," Pastor Mtenzi interjected with a broad, peaceful smile cresting his noble features. Chris flashed him a quick smile in return, his eagerness written across his face.

"And Abigail," Barry added, turning to the thin young woman before him, "I hear that Nathan has seen a lot of progress in the printing container."

"Yes," she replied, beaming. "It is exciting to see Ellen White materials printed here for the first time."

Pastor Mtenzi remained silent, but his eyes shone like stars. Abigail could hear Jessica's pleasant chatter through the open window from the clinic nearby. The faint hum of the campus four-wheeler sounded across the green circle of palm trees. She caught a glimpse of Nathan, Starla, and Daniel riding slowly to the clinic through a nearby window. *All is well in the world.*

"Do I understand correctly that you are scheduled to return to the States in January?" Barry asked.

Christopher nodded. "Yes."

"We can see that God is working and using your efforts," he repeated. "And I am asking on behalf of the mission committee if you both would consider extending your stay here in Congo."

Silence reigned while the wheels of Abigail's mind turned. In an instant, she remembered her mental wrestling with God on many mornings: mornings when she wondered if He would call her to stay in Congo permanently, mornings when she wondered whether He would preserve her from the dangers that surrounded them. Her barrage of secret fears had since been calmed by God's promises, and she had resolved to answer yes to His calling.

Is this God's call to me—to both of us? she wondered. She had almost forgotten about her inward struggles with uncertainty in the recent busy days. She had been too busy in the printing container and keeping house to think about robbers.

Christopher looked over at her questioningly, but she knew the thoughts of his heart. Throughout their time in Congo—whether they sped over rough terrain on a motorcycle or shared a pot of soup with Allen and Jessica—they had enjoyed every moment. *Christopher loves this life.*

Abigail responded slowly. "When we left Christopher's work in the States, it was with the understanding that his boss would have him back in January. I would like to touch base with his Adventist employer first. But provided that the way is clear—yes, we are willing to stay."

Pastor Mtenzi never lost the light in his eyes as he slowly leaned back in his seat. Barry typed a few words on his laptop as Keith grinned.

Suddenly, the faint sounds of distant shouting broke through the morning's peace like the crash of broken glass. Keith was in midsentence when a pale Nathan Rittenour strode up the aisle of the chapel. Although Nathan's voice was calm and quiet as usual, the impact of his words hit the gathered missionaries with staggering force.

"I'm sorry to interrupt, but there's been an accident. On the road. Someone was killed." His brow beaded with sweat. He wiped it carelessly with his calloused fingers. "We must go. Right now."

Abigail turned just in time to see Barry's face register shock and Keith's great pain. The faces of Kayumba and Joel passed through her mind. They had gone with the crew to the road. *Oh Lord, please let it not be one of them.* "Who?" she croaked out the single word.

"One of our hired men from Huit." Nathan didn't even know the man's name.

A male figure rushed to the open door of the chapel—it was Kayumba, framed in the morning light, wearing his white hard hat. His shoulders were heaving and his breath caught in gasps. Tears streamed unchecked across his face.

THE ACCIDENT

Abigail had seen Congolese with painful medical conditions, trembling with pain and nervousness before treatment. She had observed children being disciplined by Joel's wife in their front yard, yelling in protest. But never had Abigail seen a Congolese cry like this. Kayumba paused only for a moment by the open door, but the expression of grief and terror she saw written across his face would remain forever etched in her memory. With another heave of his shoulders, the man ran off.

"This meeting is adjourned," Barry stated abruptly as he rose and slipped his cell phone into his front pocket. Keith, Mtenzi, Nathan, and the Dumans rushed to the green where the climate of the campus had suddenly changed—completely—like a different world had been ushered in during their few minutes in the chapel.

Keith and Barry took off in the direction of the Mosier home. Adventist workers ran across the grass and shouted garbled warnings in Swahili. While the American missionaries stood confused and unsure, the locals pressed them with the assurance that danger was impending. They understood the culture of swift revenge, the spirit of anger in the hearts of some of their countrymen, the politically explosive atmosphere, and the likelihood of heated violence—they understood it all too well. Congo's wars were still fresh in their memory. They understood that safety was always relative and never certain.

As soon as Allen Smith heard the shouting, he ran across the green and down the campus driveway. Not far from Daniel's little sandy spot, where he liked to play on sunny afternoons, lay the body of a young man from Huit.

"Kayumba warned two of our hired men not to sit on the sides of the truck," a worker panted out the story. "They didn't listen. One fell out and was hit by the Fuso."

Allen slowed as he drew near to the accident scene. The man had been instantly killed, and there was nothing that the young doctor could do.

In front of his own brick home, Pastor Mtenzi calmly yet commandingly gave out orders, pointing with his strong brown arm. "The vehicles—we have to get them to safety in the depot, or they will be stolen when the mob comes."

Without a second's hesitation, Chris jumped on the four-wheeler that Nathan had abandoned and nearly flew across the thick grass on the green. Kayumba ran to his side when he reached the depot—a walled rectangle where the missionaries stored much of their supplies and sometimes their vehicles for security.

"Fuso, in depot," the Congolese urged in broken English.

Chris scanned the driver's seat of the heavy work truck. "No key," he gestured. "There's no key."

Leaving the Fuso where the driver, Chauffeur, had abandoned it, the two did what they could to secure the mission's valuable equipment in the walled enclosure of the depot.

Bewildered and overwhelmed, Abigail stood alone on the gravel drive as if in a dream. What could she do in this shocking, suddenly-changing world? Then Starla's voice pulled her to her senses. "Abby, come!"

Starla and Daniel were sitting in Pastor Mtenzi's vehicle in front of his house. Abigail ran to the vehicle and slammed the car door behind her. She slid onto the worn leather seat beside Starla.

"Lock all of the doors."

"What is happening?" Abigail asked.

Barry and Keith took off in the direction of the Mosier home. Everywhere across the green, she saw people running. *Congolese don't run. Not unless there's danger.*

"A mob is coming, Abby. We may not be able to get out of here in time." Her hands trembled as she locked the final door. She hugged Daniel close to her heart.

"What mob?" Abigail questioned.

"The family members of the man who died will be angry. We own the Fuso truck, and we sponsored the road work and paid the men. People won't stop to hear the whole story. They will blame us for his death. Our workers are in danger too, especially Kayumba. Pray Abby—pray, pray."

Oh Lord Jesus, what is happening? Surely this is just a terrible nightmare. Only a few moments ago, it was peaceful. Scene after scene from the past few months flashed before the young woman's mind: The burned truck in town, the volatile culture of vengeance, the people so long mistreated by Europeans. *Now we don't even know if we will escape with our lives.*

"Do you have your passport with you?" Starla's voice once again broke into her thoughts. "You need it to leave the country."

"No, it's back in our bedroom at the house," Abigail mourned. "What should I do?"

Starla hesitated. "If you want them, go now. The mob could be here at any minute."

The younger woman's hand grasped the door handle and flipped the lock. "I'm going."

"Listen, if you see the mob, come running immediately back to this car."

"I will."

"Oh, Abby," she leaned forward. "Daniel's inhalers. They're in the spare bedroom in a clear bag. Please bring his inhalers!"

As Abigail's sandals hit the grass, her feet flew and her heart pounded. She retraced the familiar shortcut that, less than an hour earlier, she had walked with her husband. With every gasp of fresh air, she breathed a prayer. *Oh Lord, I don't know if I am going to make it out of here with my life. Please stay close to us.* At least she and her fellow missionaries felt the assurance that they rested in the center of God's will. At least they were surrendered. At that moment, Abigail felt grateful that she hadn't waited until this moment to trust God with her life. She appreciated the journey of faith and trust that led her to this moment—no matter how terrifying and uncertain the future felt.

In a few moments, Abigail reached the campus road running not far from the path leading to her familiar brick home in the clearing. She scanned the road in the direction of the campus gate and saw the abandoned Fuso truck. Mamma Rebecca stood in the middle of the road by the depot, calling out to her. "Abigail!"

A string of rapid Swahili words followed Mamma Rebecca's call, but she couldn't understand them. Maybe she could if she stopped to listen, but she couldn't—not then. *I must get the passports.*

Daniel's familiar black stroller sat parked in the yard. She rushed past it and right up to the iron bars that enclosed the cement porch. And then her heart sank.

The gate was padlocked. Abigail had no keys with her and felt another overwhelming sense of confusion. She turned to look back at the gravel road just in time to see Christopher running around the corner in her direction. He had seen her running from the depot. He was coming—oh, welcome sight!

Relief flooded her face to see him. "We need to get our passports and money," she urged as he jerked a key from the pocket of his jeans and hastily unlocked the gate. Once on the concrete, Chris leaped forward and clasped the handle of their newly installed American door—only to realize that it was locked. The Rittenours had apparently locked the door after them that morning, and there was no key to be had for it. Before Abigail had time to feel disappointment, her husband had whipped out his Congolese driver's license from his wallet and picked the lock. All of his practice picking locks as a youth had paid off: the door opened in seconds, and the couple rushed inside. Every minute counted.

Chris slung a backpack around his shoulder and reached for the passports and money. *What should I take?* Abigail struggled to think clearly as she reached for a few items but forgot Daniel's all-important inhalers.

"Come on; we've got to go." Christopher rushed his wife out of the door as she took one last glance behind her at the bedroom. The mosquito net hung in billowing folds, surrounding their light blue quilt where her Bible rested, framed by the netting. She had left it there after her worship that morning.

"Wait for me," Abigail panted as she struggled to keep up with her husband's pace. He reached for her arm, and together they ran to the center of the green where the Rittenours were waiting in Pastor Mtenzi's car.

"Should we really go?" Nathan questioned Pastor Mtenzi.

"Go—get out of here," the strong Tanzanian pastor urged without hesitation. The pastor grasped his wife's hand for a moment and then helped her into the front seat of the vehicle.

Mamma Mtenzi's face was tight with concern. "Why aren't you coming with us?" she asked half questioningly, half pleadingly.

"I'm staying behind to negotiate," he said as he backed away, closing the car door between them. Nathan jumped into the driver's seat and brought the vehicle to life, while Jessica squished into the back seat with Starla, Daniel, Abigail, and Christopher. "Here," Allen said, handing Christopher a small canister of pepper spray. "I'm jumping in the back trunk, and there's a good chance that you might need this." Chris took it.

"Pray for my husband," Mamma Mtenzi begged as the Americans in the crowded car pulled out into the drive. "Please pray that he is safe. I don't know what the mob will do to him."

Starla nodded vigorously with her white hands still clasped around Daniel. "We are praying, Mamma Mtenzi."

A few seconds of silence passed. "Are you OK, Mamma?" Allen asked Mrs. Mtenzi.

No words came in response—only a sigh from the front seat.

"Your husband is so brave," Starla spoke up.

Jessica's pretty young face was solemn, and she said little. Allen remained collected and reassuring as he verbally guided Nathan every so often down the winding drive. Nathan gripped the steering wheel with resolve, unsure of what lay ahead. He slowed when Allen warned that they were approaching the accident scene, but his jaw was set in determination. He would do everything in his power to get his loved ones out of this situation. Maybe God would work a miracle, too, for they would need one to escape to the city, where it was safer.

Suddenly, Mamma Mtenzi drew in her breath sharply. Tears streamed across her cheeks as they passed the dreadful scene. Leaving the crumpled, lifeless body on the ground felt so very *wrong*. Somewhere in the village of Huit, a family would be grieving. Abigail felt upset with a culture that prevented her from grieving with them without having to run for her own life.

The voices of urgent, unashamed prayer filled the vehicle. Abigail felt a desperate need for the prayers of her friends and family, but she realized that it was night on the other side of the world. "Pray for us," she texted anyway. "We are in danger and don't know if we will escape safely."

THE ACCIDENT

Starla bravely held her young son and prayed aloud. "Dear Father, please keep Pastor Mtenzi and others safe on campus. Be with the young man's family as they mourn. Please keep us safe by sending Your angels."

Angels. *Are they here?* Abigail's eyes traveled across the car. *I can't see them. Surely, His angels must be here with us.* Angels had visited Kisangani before and delivered a message of Jesus' soon return to little children. Like an army, they had surrounded missionaries who slept unaware as witches approached. Today, as God's people faced impending danger, His angels were needed again. With all of the faith in her heart that she could muster, she breathed another word of prayer. *I don't see the angels, but I believe that they are here.*

Starla's thoughts ran in a similar direction, like a cord of gold leading through a black tunnel. She and Abigail mentally grasped it with desperate strength. "Remember Nathan, how the angels surrounded you and the others at the beginning in Kisangani, how the witches saw 'men in white' protecting us. The angels are with us now," Starla encouraged.

Oh Lord, I don't see Your angels, Abigail silently confessed again. *But I believe.*

The missionaries held their breath around each bend in the road, never sure if the next corner would reveal a roadblock of some kind or a mob to prevent them from passing. So far, the path before them remained clear. The usual travelers on foot at that time of day dove for the jungle as they rushed past.

"Oh no," Starla breathed. A large truck had gotten stuck in the middle of the road ahead of them. The roadwork that the crew had accomplished the day before had made the way easier, but mud remained in the untouched places after the night rain.

Nathan stepped out of the vehicle and surveyed the road for options to pass. Time was of the essence. The longer they waited, the greater the chance that trouble would follow.

"Be careful, Nathan!" Starla called out.

Nathan planted his feet on the road and hesitated for only a moment. "I believe that there is just enough room to pass. We really have no other choice than to pass. But this is going to be bumpy," he warned as he gripped the steering wheel once again.

"We don't care about the bumps," Starla quickly replied.

"Where are Keith and the others?" Abigail anxiously asked as they bounced past the stalled truck.

"They are in a vehicle maybe five minutes behind us," Allen said from the back. "I've been in touch with him via my cell phone."

The rest of the way to town, the road was incredibly bumpy but fairly dry. When they reached the outskirts of Kisangani, Nathan pulled over beside a cluster of market booths.

"Are we stopping here?" Mamma Mtenzi asked tensely, clearly eager to find a safer place.

"I think we should wait for Keith and the others to catch up and then find a hotel," Nathan replied.

Allen clamped the phone to his ear, dialing Keith. "Hey Keith, how's it going?" The young doctor paused, then shouted at Nathan. "Keep driving," his voice increased in volume. "Go fast! Keith is being followed."

Abigail gazed through her nearby window. *How incredible that a place that once appeared friendly and comfortable could so quickly feel this frightening and dangerous.*

Nathan found a gated hotel in Kisangani, believing that it would keep them safer. The group prayed again before venturing from the confines of the vehicle and then suppressed their fears as they stepped outside into the bright sunlight.

In a few minutes, the group was led to a hotel room. Nathan quickly locked the door and closed the curtains on the windows. Mamma Mtenzi sank into a chair and clutched her cell phone, waiting for a phone call from her husband.

When everyone had set down their few belongings, they knelt in a circle on the cold tile floor and prayed with all their hearts. They prayed for Kayumba, Joel, and the other campus workers who faced danger because they were connected with the Seventh-day Adventist mission. They prayed for brave Pastor Mtenzi, who stayed behind to see if he could save the mission campus from destruction. And they prayed for Keith and Tammy, Barry, Alvina, and the children who were still in the confines of a vehicle and trying to escape danger.

"Please thwart the plans of the enemy," Abigail petitioned. "We know that love is stronger than hate and that truth will triumph in the end."

CHAPTER 16

A MIRACULOUS ESCAPE

When tragic news of the accident reached the busy Mosier household, Tammy felt completely unprepared for a hasty departure. They had recently finished breakfast. Alvina, always attentive, had offered her help with the cleanup, and Tammy was embarking on the process of getting her four squirming children dressed when Keith rushed through their doorway with his father close behind.

Tammy acted quickly. She hurriedly finished dressing Anna and reached for a large square of cornbread baked the day before. Who knew when they would be able to return home safely or when they could obtain food for the children? Keith pulled the family vehicle up to the door while Tammy spent several minutes grabbing various items she thought they might need. When the family—together with Barry and Alvina—loaded into the vehicle, they were five minutes behind the first vehicle containing the Rittenours, Dumans, and Smiths.

News of the deadly accident spread rapidly. By the time the Mosiers traveled painfully by the accident scene, two relatives of the deceased young man stood by. Keith glanced in the rearview mirror with searching eyes. Within moments, he saw the relatives hailing moto-taxis on the road nearby. The motorcyclists followed at a rapid pace, pushing Keith to the highest speed he had ever traveled on the winding road. "We are going to the police station in Kisangani," Keith told the others. "We can safely talk about the accident with the man's relatives there."

Seeing that Nathan had successfully traveled around the stopped truck, Keith drove as quickly as he dared through the narrow space. Then, a second delay appeared in sight, forcing their vehicle to a crawl. A single man blocked the way as he slowly pushed a heavy load of charcoal over the road's incline.

"I'll help," Barry jumped from the vehicle. Adding his strength to the load, he helped to push it up and out of the way. The motorcyclists roared into view around a bend just as Barry slammed the car door behind him. He was safely inside.

They surged ahead, and the race was on again. As the vehicle reached the edge of Kisangani, the two motorcyclist drivers began to yell: "Don't let them get away! These Americans killed someone!"

A following of motorcyclists behind the vehicle doubled in moments. Realizing that his family continued to be in danger, Keith sought a chance to lose the foreboding group behind his back bumper. He was forced to drive slower now that he was in the city but managed to quickly turn down a side road that sometimes served as a shortcut. Keith had used it before. But as he barreled down the side path, the vehicle was forced to stop suddenly. The way was completely blocked by road construction. A crew had left a mountain of debris in the way, and Keith could not drive over it nor slip past it. Suddenly, they were hedged in on every side by men who quickly formed a violent mob.

The missionary father's heart sank. He could see no earthly way out of the situation. No amount of hopefulness or positivity could remedy their risk. The vehicle was instantly surrounded. If he backed up, he risked hitting someone and would only double their fury. Men pounded on the doors and windows, screaming at the missionaries who had devoted their lives to bringing them hope.

Anna whimpered and buried her face in Tammy's hands. Shiloh began to cry. "Jesus is still with us, Shiloh," Tammy spoke calmly, reassuringly.

Alvina understood the bleakness of the situation. Pulling out her iPad, she began to type a message to her son—her beloved Peter in the States. She only had time to write two brief sentences: "We may die today. We are ready."

The fate of the vehicle's occupants appeared grim when jugs of gasoline were passed through the irrational, angry mob. If God did not intervene, the mission's Toyota Land Cruiser would become a blackened frame of metal.

"Mamma," young Shiloh said, breathing quickly. "This reminds me of the story Grandma read—the one about John Huss."

Alvina looked through the window glass into the face of a Congolese. His features were contorted in rage as he repeatedly raised his fist, slamming it down on the window as if to break it. The older woman hesitated for a moment as if unsure how to respond. For one facing a living nightmare only inches outside the vehicle's window glass, she felt an incredible amount of God's peace. Her face relaxed. Turning her head to gaze at the angry mobster through the window, she smiled and slowly nodded her head. "It's OK," she told him through the glass. "It's going to be OK."

Suddenly, the intensity of his expression vanished. The bulging veins around his neck relaxed. It was as if an evil spirit left him at that moment, and he slunk out of sight, disappearing into the crowd.

Instantly, he was replaced by another raving in anger. "It's OK," Alvina made eye contact and smiled lovingly at this man too. "It's OK."

A MIRACULOUS ESCAPE

In the face of death, Alvina could love her enemy. The foundation of her faith was strong. The peace she knew in her prayers on quiet Congo mornings was the same peace that carried her through these tense moments. Three times, the love in her eyes sent a volatile man backing away from the window.

In answer to the prayers ascending heavenward, two policemen fought their way through the angry mob. They were unarmed, but they pressed their way through until they reached the missionary's vehicle. The reputation of a police officer in Kisangani was held in low regard, but their position of power commanded respect. Some were ruthless, and many were greedy, but the two officers who came to the Mosiers' rescue were brave men.

When Keith saw the men in uniform, he knew that they could help. In the Congolese culture, they were allowed to take liberties in the line of duty that the average citizen could not. Barry opened his door to allow the officers to enter the vehicle, and when he did, the crowd surged forward. Before he could blink, a hand reached into his shirt pocket and snatched his cell phone. He reached for it in the thief's grasp and felt his fingers make contact with its smooth surface, but the phone slipped out of his hands and disappeared into the rabble.

Once inside, one officer slipped into the front seat where Keith sat and immediately took over the wheel. Barry and the policeman in the back seat were then faced with a serious problem—how to close the vehicle door shut. Barry and his police friend gripped the handle and pulled with all their might, while the mob pulled with a frenzy in the opposite direction.

Somehow, Barry and the policeman managed to shut and lock the door again. "We must have had angel help," Tammy breathed. "I don't know how we could close the door with so many pulling on the other side."

"I wonder if our policemen are angels," Alvina pondered. "They are potentially risking their lives to save us."

The roar of the mob diminished with the addition of the policemen in the car. The two men dressed in deep blue could legally harm others in the line of duty with no repercussions, and the people knew this. When their new driver confidently backed up, the thick mass of people was forced to part ways to avoid being hit.

With a huge sigh of relief, the missionaries reached the police station. Keith found the deceased man's relatives already waiting for him there, and they met in a private room to discuss what had happened. Keith saw no anger written across their faces. They had been touched by the ministry of the Americans on the campus and trusted that they were honorable people. When Keith learned the name of the man who died, he wept.

"They called him Soni," Keith told the others when he and his family reached their gated hotel in Kisangani later that day under police escort. "He was twenty-two years old. I've known his family for years, and at one point, we helped a relative of his with medical treatment for a burn. They know us and that we truly care for the people here. Although they are grieving, they understand that what happened was an accident." A mixture of grief and relief was in his voice. The angry rabble was composed of out-of-control people looking for a situation where they could release their pent-up anger.

"Have we heard any news from campus?" Allen asked Keith expectantly.

Keith shook his head slightly. "Not much. I am hoping to hear from Pastor Mtenzi soon."

"I'm hungry, Mommy," Anna said, tugging at Tammy's jean dress. Tammy reached into her satchel and presented the cornbread from that morning.

Abigail dug through her backpack on the floor, finding items that she had packed for previous trips (like the one to Isangi). What a treasure these few leftover items were now! It felt like Christmas to Abigail as she unzipped every pocket. The best find of all was a variety of granola bars from the States. She and Alvina shared similar health allergies, making some food items such as Congolese bread and pasta off-limits. *I'm so glad to share these with Alvina.* She felt certain that the few bites of nourishment they provided would go a long way in the coming days ahead—provided that the mob didn't find the displaced missionaries again first.

Even though Abigail had little more than the clothing on her back, she thanked God that their immediate danger had passed. "I know that we have a lot of items left behind at the house, but I'd be happy to leave it all behind forever in exchange for life," she confided to Christopher. "I'm so thankful that He preserved us."

"Me too," he said squeezing her hand in his.

When Tammy joined the adults watching the children munch on cornbread around a low-lying coffee table, she told Abigail, "The Lord saved us from the mob today, but we are not entirely out of the woods yet. We need to keep a low profile. Avoid being seen much by people who may cause trouble." Tammy shivered slightly, caught in a breeze from the hotel air conditioner, but Abigail doubted that her tremor was from the cold. Tammy's eyes looked exhausted, and her shoulders slumped slightly. She had nothing more to her name than the clothes on her back, and for all she knew, her family's home on campus and investment of over ten years was by now reduced to piles of rubble.

Keith ordered several plates of food from the hotel kitchen, but most of the adults weren't hungry. Mamma Mtenzi remained glued to her chair, still hoping and praying that her husband was safe amidst the probable chaos on campus. While the missionaries had narrowly escaped with their lives, the challenges for those who remained behind earlier that morning had just begun.

CHAPTER 17

LOVE REVEALED IN CRISIS

When news of the accident reached Mamma Rose's ears at the Barry Mosier school, she ran for her toddler and rushed all students from the classroom.

"Go home or go hide!" she cried.

Children scampered over the hard-packed earth and passed the unfinished well on the nearby rise. Some crashed into the thick jungle nearby, being too far from their homes to return quickly. Other young people belonging to the Adventist families who lived on campus ran up the winding driveway, only to stumble upon the terrible accident scene. Kayumba's boys were among those who passed the body.

When Kayumba could have vanished into the jungle and left the missionaries' investment of sweat and dreams to burn, he remained. Although he was distraught and fearful, Kayumba felt a strong loyalty to the mission and the people who operated it. After seeing the missionaries leave in their vehicles, he ran to the Dumans' house and tore damp clothes off the laundry line. Seeing Daniel's stroller sitting in the yard, he wheeled it into a nearby Congolese home for safekeeping.

Meanwhile, Mtenzi learned that Chauffeur had not disappeared into the bush as many had assumed. Instead, someone had spotted Chauffeur slipping into Keith's office, where he locked himself inside. He apparently trusted that the missionaries wouldn't deliver him to an angry mob to be killed. Mtenzi met him quickly in the office and retrieved the key to the Fuso truck. The Tanzanian felt relieved when he knew that all mission vehicles were secured in the depot.

If the village of Huit had been situated between the campus and Kisangani, the missionaries would have met with an almost guaranteed roadblock. News of the accident traveled there swiftly. Papi, a friend of the mission who lived in Huit, was in the middle of brickmaking when he heard what had happened. The man leaped up. "The mission is in trouble," he said. "I must go." Friends from several villages ran to the green circle of palms in the center of campus.

"We must lay a strategy to help the missionaries," Papi urged. "Trouble-makers will be here very soon."

"I came as fast as I could to protect and save my friends," another villager from Huit explained.

"We must call for help from the police," Himba, the old village chief of Huit said firmly.

"Here," Papi reached deeply into the pocket of his faded pants. "I don't have much money, but take this to get help for us." He pressed the currency into a trusted church leader's hand, who quickly ran to find a moto-taxi.

As people began to gather, Pastor Mtenzi decided to hide out of sight. He slipped behind the greenery on a hill overlooking the green circle and quickly dialed his wife. "Our campus workers have set up a barricade across from the office building, hoping to prevent angry troublemakers from entering," he reported. "They figure that the bad boys in the area will steal and destroy mission homes. Please keep us in prayer."

Soon it became apparent that any person who harbored enmity, bitterness, jealousy, or anger in their heart against God's people welcomed the opportunity to loot and destroy. A crowd of ruffians clashed with the mission's loyal friends at the metal gate and overpowered them. Angry men stormed across the thick green grass of the palm circle, approaching the brick houses. Many hands picked up stones from the drive and hurled them through the windows of Pastor Mtenzi's home, finally breaking in to loot.

Meanwhile, the overpowered Congolese at the gate scattered, stationing themselves at each missionary home in hopes that they could prevent damages.

"Our friends are exceedingly brave," Pastor Mtenzi marveled from his observation point. "I see a campus guard walking from group to group, trying to reason with the people. Our people are trying to prevent more trouble from happening. They are being a voice for those who can't speak."

While homes belonging to the American missionaries were especially targeted, the Congolese Adventists who lived nearby were remembered by the ruffians too. One wife was overseeing a pot of beans boiling on a charcoal burner when several troublemakers ran up. With a single heave, the two men dumped the precious food over the hard-packed ground.

The troublemakers found Kayumba in his home, where Esther and their children were quietly hiding out of sight.

"Kayumba!" The Congolese heard his name yelled.

A nervous sweat broke out on the young father's face. His history with the mission, the responsibility he was given by the missionaries, and his leadership on the road crew: all of these factors put his life in danger.

The men would break down his mahogany door sooner than later. Hearing his name again, he stumbled out into the light. Esther joined him on the cement porch and helplessly watched the confrontation that ensued. If the men killed Kayumba, she knew that she would probably be next.

The man who immediately faced Kayumba wielded a machete. "Soni was killed today. You deserve to die, Kayumba."

Could he face death with peace? He had spent long hours working side by side with American missionaries who were willing to risk everything to bring the gospel to his people. He had accompanied them to many Seventh-day Adventist church services where God's messages were preached with power. The message of love that the missionaries taught—was it strong enough to combat such hate and fury that faced him on his own front porch? *Love is the law of heaven. Love is more powerful than hate.*

Kayumba trusted himself to God's mercy, realizing that he was helpless to control the events that surrounded him. At that moment, his eyes unleashed a fresh set of tears. "My heart is grieved that Soni has died," he said, weeping. "I am so sorry that the accident happened."

The angry man paused with his machete poised. Instantly, the Spirit of God seemed to constrain the hardened heart. His hand fell to his side, and he turned away.

Kayumba watched with wonder as his would-be attacker disappeared from sight and joined others on a jog to another house in hopes of stealing more. Then his eyes locked with Esther's. Praise God; they had been spared. The campus worker straightened his shoulders, heart overflowing with a new appreciation to God, who so obviously spared his life.

Kayumba stepped down from his porch. There was a work to do for God, and the mission must be protected. Kayumba was a changed man.

The leader of the rowdy, thieving crowd knew the campus well. He had worked for the Mosier family and fed their dog daily—until he was laid off after repeatedly stealing from them. It was Prence. Charging to the forefront, he led a ragtag group of men to their target home.

Along the way, they paused at Nathan Rittenour's empty house. They could easily see that it was swept clean for repairs and contained little of value. However, noticing the behemoth generator used to power the printing container nearby, their eyes brightened. A perfect thing to steal! It would be worth a lot of money if sold in Kisangani. The men pounced on it, heaving and pushing with all their might—but the generator barely budged. In frustration and disgust, they knocked the generator onto its side and moved on.

Seeing the friendly home of Keith Mosier brought fresh memories to Prence's mind. Hate and bitterness spewed from his lips. Finding a piece of metal nearby, he and others broke the welding that held the iron bars on the side door into the house while another group managed to break through a bedroom window. While Simba, the Mosier's large American dog, would have made the mob think twice with his barking, the dog was silent as a mouse. Prence had fed Simba daily during his employment on the campus: the dog made no protest.

It was probably to Simba's credit that he remained quiet as the looting began. Papi from Huit followed the mob and attempted to prevent the stealing but was forced to retreat when someone injured him with a machete. He had risked his life for the sake of preserving his friends' belongings.

Kayumba hurried back and forth between the waves of looters who arrived on campus and tried to reason with them. "The missionaries are here to serve. What have they done against you?"

In Africa's heart of darkness, where hate and bitterness seemed to reign, light shone in the spirit of precious people who refused to leave without advocating for God's cause. When the devil's fury unleashed itself upon the mission station in Kisangani, heavenly angels were there. When the American missionaries had no voice to speak and no power to prevent the onslaught, Congolese who loved the same God advocated in their stead. In place of hate, there was love, and on a terrifying day, courage and faith surged to the forefront.

The scene Pastor Mtenzi observed across campus was both beautiful and dangerous at the same time. He heard the voices of both men and women who were touched with the sweet spirit of Jesus, endeavoring to reason with the unruly mob led by Prence and his gang. Others began negotiating with the dead man's family, assuring them that their temporal needs and funeral expenses would be covered. Thankfully, help to disperse the looting was only a few paces away. The church leader from Huit was able to find help from the police, who pulled into the campus drive on motorcycles.

When Pastor Mtenzi saw that the mob had dispersed with the presence of the police, he crept down from the hillside and carefully crossed campus. Before he left to hail a motorcyclist on the winding road to town, an Adventist friend spotted him. "Well, Pastor Mtenzi," the man said, "after today, we know this—God's angels are with us."

"We know that this is true," the missionary said, thankful that no one that afternoon had been seriously injured.

Still on campus, Esther carefully stored the clothing Kayumba stripped from the Dumans' clothesline inside her house. Loyal hands moved the conglomerate of items on the porch to the inside of the Dumans' house, aware that any loose items would disappear if left out. Another Adventist worker swept the porch clean.

The campus had not yet returned to its characteristic quiet. Ruffians returned in waves to the campus, hoping to steal more from the Mosier home. The police stationed themselves on the lawn and commanded them to disperse, but the irrational group refused. Finally, an officer in blue set off a tear-gas grenade.

"We are sorry, we are sorry!" The suddenly penitent people obediently melted away as they coughed and wiped their eyes.

The looting was over. The power of God's staying hand had preserved His people. The campus finally quieted as night settled over the jungle forests. Only this evening, the missionary houses were empty. Congolese workers and their families slipped out of their homes to survey the damage to the missionary homes and wondered what the future would hold. Several police officers lingered to guard against further looting.

The day of November 1 had reached a close. In one day, lives were changed forever. The chapel stood silent. But the words of wise Elder Tembo seemed to echo over the rough brick walls: "In a crisis, love comes to the forefront."

With a new understanding now, the Adventist believers in the area would read the account in Scripture of when Jesus faced a mob. When sinners were doomed to be crushed by sin and death, when danger was imminent, Christ looked in the face of all the rage and hatred that Satan could muster and had faith and peace. His love, without a doubt, is stronger than life itself. Characterized by the humble lives of the Congolese who accepted Christ, there resided this same powerful love undisputed.

CHAPTER 18

DECISIONS

As the hours passed in the Kisangani hotel, the time was largely spent kneeling on the cold floor, pacing the hallways, and calling loved ones in the States with the news. The air was thick with a myriad of questions—most to which the missionaries had no answers. Was the investment of ten years in Congo made up of broken brick and ashes now? Were their Adventist workers safe? What had become of the printing container? Would it ever be safe enough to return?

The group was still too shocked by the morning's events to weep. Jessica pulled out her laptop and edited countless photos from her previous travels. Barry worked to clear all of his information from his stolen phone. Just outside the front door on a small porch, Christopher, Allen, and Keith discussed the lack of food and other essentials, while Shiloh, Caleb, and Anna leaped across the tile floor and prattled, perhaps seeking a way to relieve their own stress.

"Can we go outside to the porch to see Daddy?" Caleb asked as he tugged at the doorknob.

Tammy quickly shook her head, breaking away from a conversation. "Not right now, Caleb." Then she returned to talking in low tones. "I'm still in shock. Abigail, we could have died today."

"The men should come inside," Starla said with conviction as she entered from an adjoining room. "I don't think the general public should know that we are staying in this hotel."

Tammy agreed. Abigail hurried to the small table and chairs just outside the door and looked at her husband, imploring, "Would you please come in?"

She could tell that he felt no concern. "I think it's fine to be out here, Abby," he said, shrugging slightly. "But I will if you would prefer it."

He would do it for her. Her only response was a look of gratefulness. Allen and Keith followed Christopher inside just before the whirring of a motorcycle sounded in the courtyard. Chris parted the window curtains and turned to face the living room. "Pastor Mtenzi is here!"

DECISIONS

Mamma Mtenzi jumped up from her chair and fairly flew through the door into the scorching afternoon sunlight. She clung to the pastor as they embraced.

The men met Pastor Mtenzi partway and ushered him into their living quarters. "Pastor Mtenzi," Keith said as he grasped the fellow missionary's hand. "Our prayers were with you. We are so glad that you are all right."

"Instead of fearing, we can take heart today," Pastor Mtenzi assured them. He relayed the news from campus when they had returned indoors. The expectant band of missionary families circled around him.

"Our friends spent four hours on the campus, telling the mob of our witness and our God. The little money that they had, they gave for us. Several narrowly escaped with their lives. Kayumba was one of the bravest among them, rushing from one group of looters to another to try to bring peace."

"Do you know what happened to the driver, Chauffeur?" Starla asked.

"He hid in Keith's office for the afternoon undetected: things would not have gone well for him if he had been found. He told me that he would present himself to the police in town for his own safety until people calm down."

"That's a relief," Nathan responded, rubbing the palms of his hands together. "Hopefully, that happens soon so that we can return to campus."

"When do you suppose we *can* return?" Keith asked the pastor as he took crying Talitha from Tammy's extended arms.

Pastor Mtenzi paused. "Not for a few days, at least. The police are guarding the homes, but we do not know what the future holds. There are still angry people who want to blame us for the accident."

"The well at the school," Nathan said, his thoughts jumping forward. He was ever the visionary. "Can we not finish it? Every time passersby on the road drink from it, they will remember us and that we care."

Pastor Mtenzi slowly shook his head. "Finishing the well at this point would be culturally disrespectful. As the family grieves and prepares for the funeral, it is best that we express our sympathy by grieving too and laying aside other projects."

Life had never felt more appreciated, more precious than it did to the small company that night. Confused and exhausted, they closed the evening with a prayer and parting words.

Pastor Mtenzi concluded the evening gathering. "I'd like to encourage each couple to talk tonight and pray about the future. While we face a lot of unknowns, we do have some decisions to make."

The air conditioner in the Dumans' bedroom produced more noise than it did cold air. Finally, alone with her husband, Abigail collapsed as her mind reeled from the events of the day.

"Why can't I grieve that young man's death without having to run for my own life?" she demanded through tears that quickly began falling. "I can hardly bear it."

Christopher had no answer. His eyes solemnly searched hers. "I don't understand it either," he admitted.

"If I could only have one more day of work in the printing container," she thought aloud. "If I could have just a little longer to print one more book."

"You did what you could. The rest is up to God."

The couple sat under their mosquito net together as Christopher looked through phone pictures that chronicled their time in Congo: Well drilling at the Barry Mosier school. Joel, grinning with a shovel in his hand while standing in a patch of thick mud. The motorcycle trip to Isangi. Sunlight glinting across the waters of the Congo from an overloaded dugout. Beautiful faces of Congolese children with a lot of hope and yet facing a lot of life challenges.

Abigail understood her husband's thoughts. He loved this land and the beautiful people who lived here. His hopes and dreams for the next few months were slowly fading, and the expression on his fine features told her so. He wanted to be there to preach the evangelistic series in Kisangani as planned. He wanted to see the baptism of their two neighbor ladies who responded to his call after a sermon in the chapel. He wanted to pull the handle on the well pump at the schoolhouse and see fresh, clean water gushing from it for the children.

Abigail hugged his arm instinctively. "I'm so sorry," she breathed. "I'm disappointed too." They wept together.

In a room one floor above them, little Daniel called out in his sleep. "Safe, safe!" he repeated. Starla listened to her little one's breathing, praying that he would not need the inhalers they no longer had. She and Nathan went through their own process of mourning for all that was lost that day—for the death of the young man from Huit and for the end of an era where Kisangani felt safe to them. As safe as it had felt before, at least.

With the kids quietly sleeping, Keith and Tammy talked well into the night. In his own room, Barry fell to his knees in prayer. And the night wore on.

The hotel breakfast the next morning afforded some nourishment to the missionaries, but Abigail picked through the few items that she could eat. Aside from several slices of pineapple and avocado, there was nothing that her food allergies would allow her to have.

And Alvina is even worse off than me, she thought. *She is even sensitive to rice, which is such a common staple here.* After digging into her backpack, Abigail found several granola bars. "Here, Alvina," she said as she slipped them into her hand. "I think we'll need these for a little something extra."

DECISIONS

The older woman looked up gratefully. "Are you sure? How special—I will treasure these."

When breakfast was over, the Rittenour, Mosier, Mtenzi, and Duman families gathered in the living room to discuss plans for the near future. Each adult recalled and connected the events of the day before, including Alvina, who rehearsed her strange experience facing the mob with a smile and a nod.

Then it was Nathan's turn to speak. "You know that if the locations had been different—if Huit was situated between Kisangani and us instead of farther out into the bush, there would have been no way through." Nathan tapped his fingers on the glass table in front of him.

"Some things make more sense to me now," Abigail reflected. "Early this week, I felt a strange sort of urgency as I worked in the printing container."

"Keith and I felt the same way," Tammy assured her.

"It was a miracle that we were all together at the time of the accident," Starla said. "Someone could have easily been in town and completely unaware of what happened—until they returned and stumbled upon the danger where they would have been stuck."

"What are your plans for the immediate future?" Barry directed his question to Pastor Mtenzi.

"I shall stay here and continue to help the grieving family," the man replied. "I know that I am needed and must stay." He turned to his wife by his side expectantly.

"I know that God sent us here," Mamma Mtenzi began, "and I am not running away. But there is a wound in my heart, and I do not have peace enough yet to stay. My home country is not so volatile. If an accident happened there, it would not have been this way. I have decided to visit our children for their graduation from school abroad. When the peace that I need returns, I will come back to continue the work that God has directed us to do."

Keith nodded understandingly. "My dad, Barry, will return to the States early. Alvina will stay with us, whatever we decide to do. I believe that the rest of us are still praying for wisdom to make the right choice. While we're hopeful that we can return to campus soon, we really don't know what the future holds."

Several hours into the morning, Keith caught wind of a dismaying rumor circulating in Kisangani. Some people were saying that the American missionaries had intentionally arranged for Soni's death and were hardly different from the Europeans who mistreated Congolese in the past.

When Tammy and Keith ran to the market in search of a few necessities, they were recognized as the white missionaries who caused Soni's death. One stranger locked eyes with Tammy and raised his fist, shaking it in the air.

Tammy shrank back, surprised to find such animosity in a single person she had never met before.

"Let others go to the market for you," Pastor Mtenzi urged when he considered the rumor's impact and heard Tammy's story. "The truth will be known in the end, but tensions are high right now. You are not completely safe here."

News of the accident had spread not only through Kisangani but across the world. Supporters of the mission from Australia and America contacted Barry in confusion. Did all the missionaries survive? Was the campus secure? Would this event spell the end of Adventist presence in the area?

"I think that it would be a good idea for us to take a group picture," Barry suggested. "That way, everyone will see that we are all right and smiling. I'll post it to social media and make sure that it's sent out to donors later."

Still emotionally exhausted, the missionary wives didn't feel like smiling yet—or venturing from the hotel room to a place where the lighting was better for a photo.

"You may not feel like smiling, but you are alive." Keith's words rang true in the already humid morning air.

The group emerged into the light of the courtyard. The women hastily circled out of sight from the well-traveled public road beyond the open hotel gate while the men followed at a slower pace. At one point, Starla and Abigail found themselves walking alone over a stone pathway through a lush garden.

"Hold my hand, Abby," Starla said. Trembling slightly from the traumatic events of the day before, they pressed on together.

Keith slipped his arm around Tammy as the missionaries gathered for the photo. Most in the group were still wearing the clothes they had escaped in the day before. Alvina stood beside Abigail, wearing a leopard print dress that Mamma Mtenzi had recently bought in the market. The taller men, Allen and Christopher, stood behind and beside Abigail as Jessica snapped the picture. Shiloh's mass of golden curls beautifully framed her tender face as she clutched the folds of her sundress.

That hazy photo of the mission team in the hotel garden captured many tired faces who were only beginning to smile again. It felt like much more than a picture to Abigail. *It is a remembrance*, she later thought, *an example of God's love, which makes us all family, and a tribute to the power of God to preserve us all alive.*

CHAPTER 19

KINDNESS COMES BACK

Days passed in the hotel as the group of missionaries prayed and considered their future. With the approach of Congo's yearly politically turbulent time, many of the families were inclined to return to the United States for a brief reprieve.

Meanwhile, their Congolese church family did not forget the missionaries in their adversity. Their Congolese translator, Alan (who had translated for Christopher and Abigail when they spoke in the Kisangani church), was among the first to visit the hotel and offer his services. He and Mamma Mtenzi soon set off to find baby diapers and toothpaste in the city.

No sooner had the two left when another visitor arrived. "Abby, Kayumba is here!" Christopher's eyes brightened as he beckoned her. "Come; he's on the upper level of the hotel."

The couple raced up the flight of outdoor stairs with lightning speed. They found Kayumba standing outside of Nathan and Starla's room and eagerly grasped his hand in greeting. Abigail wished that she were fluent in Swahili to adequately express her sympathy and gratitude.

"How is your family faring?" Nathan was asking.

"Esther is OK. The children are shaken up by what happened, especially after walking by the accident scene," Kayumba added softly. "But we will be all right."

Nathan turned to Abigail. "Kayumba and our translator, Alan, want to return to campus and bring some of our belongings back to us. Do you have a list of things you need from your house?"

Before Alan pulled away on a motorcycle, Chris recalled that he still had no key to their house door. "Alan, I don't know if the door is locked to the house or not, but if it is, this is what you can do." He pulled a familiar card from his wallet and demonstrated the process.

Alan nodded. "OK. We will be back in a few hours."

Upon reaching the campus by motorcycle, the two men approached the Dumans' house. The door was locked, and Alan fiddled with the card for several minutes with no luck. Finally, Kayumba bounded to his side and reached for the card. "Kristoff has shown me before," he explained. Soon they were inside and stuffing a garbage bag full of clothing.

The two men enlisted Mamma Rebecca's and Mamma Nikke's help in packing up some items from the Mosiers' home.

"The Mosiers need their nicest clothes," Mamma Nikke murmured as she sorted through the children's bedrooms. After folding and packing every Sabbath outfit for the Mosiers that she could find, she moved on to the kitchen. In the bag went the few pots and pans left behind from the looters. "Alvina will want her tea, of course," the slim woman muttered as she ran to the lemongrass patch.

When the bags of items arrived at the hotel on the back of a motorcycle, it felt like Christmas. "I never thought that I would see these clothes again," Abigail exclaimed when she found a favorite dress. "Kayumba must have wiped our shelves clean."

"I am relieved to have clothes for the children again," Tammy said prematurely as she began to unpack a black trash bag. "Oh, Mamma Nikke!" she suddenly exclaimed.

"What?" Alvina drew near.

"She was ever so thoughtful to pack us our best clothes. But I had hoped to have cool, comfortable ones—especially for the children. These are Sabbath dresses."

Abigail looked down at her own pile of clothes. "Tammy, this shirt would look lovely on you," she held one out. "I really don't need it."

Tammy and Alvina were both hesitant to accept them but couldn't refuse each article of clothing Abigail held up. "Kayumba gave us more clothes than we actually need, and I'm so glad that we can share them with you." Abigail flashed one of her first smiles since the accident. Being very slim herself, she even found a few items that might fit young Shiloh, who was tall for her age.

"Look!" Alvina's eyes widened as she sorted through Tammy's items. "Fresh lemongrass! Oh, Mamma Nikke." Her gentle laugh echoed across the room. "She figured that I couldn't go without my tea."

Just then, Abigail pulled her Bible from the bag. "Thank you," she whispered in gratefulness. "How thoughtful."

Starla looked quite pleased as she finished unpacking her own bag from campus. "There are plenty of clothes for us here. Also, we now have Daniel's inhalers," she reported, smiling widely. "Just knowing that we have them if needed will help me sleep much better at night."

A strange switch in roles happened as the missionaries waited in the hotel. The ministry of their Adventist friends continued to touch them as the days passed. Local church leaders—who had been touched by the ministry of the mission—stopped by the hotel to show respect and sympathy in their own quiet way. Tammy ushered one Congolese couple into the air-conditioned living room, talking in Swahili about the accident.

"We are so sorry that this happened," the man said as he slowly shook his head. "Can we pray with you?"

Abigail bowed her head, listening to each Swahili word that fell from his lips. Although Swahili used to sound like garbled mumble-jumble, each word was separate and distinct to her now. Although she could still only understand a little, she knew that he spoke words of blessing and petition that God would continue His work among the Congolese.

When the couple turned to go, they left behind a sack of freshly roasted peanuts and a bunch of bananas. *This was probably all they had.* Abigail looked down at the sack of peanuts, still warm in her hands, and recalled the day that she and Christopher had shared their beans with Joel's hungry family. *I came here to this country to bless these people*, she thought, *to share the blessing of good food, clean water, and heavenly love with others. And today, we are the ones hungry, temporarily displaced, and ministered to by our Congolese family.* The realization touched her to the core. *They are showering heavenly love on us.*

As Keith explained the tricky situation we faced on campus to the hotel owner, he found a sympathizing ear. The owner was a wealthy Muslim who had assisted Congo Frontline Missions in the past and understood the volatile unpredictability present in many African countries. "I have several houses on a piece of property by the river," he rubbed his Buddha belly with a smile that revealed a gold-capped tooth. "You all are welcome to stay there. It is quite safe and secure—so much so that our governor will be staying there on the compound tomorrow night."

Keith discussed the proposition further with Nathan and decided that a move from the hotel would be wise, provided that the compound was truly what his Muslim friend described. He decided to take a short trip across town to see for himself. The men were tired of being cooped up in their rooms, and Christopher jumped at the opportunity to escape the confines of the hotel.

"Please be careful." Abigail's eyes lingered on Christopher as he prepared to leave. "I heard that someone on a street corner in the city raised a fist at one of our team members already. People are still unhappy and don't know the full truth. Be careful to stay safe. I don't know what I'd do without you."

"Don't worry. I'll be back," Chris replied, eager to leave. "Keith and Allen are waiting for me in the car. It won't take long to check the new place out."

With a few glances at the finely furnished house by the Congo River, the men quickly agreed that a move from the hotel to the house was in order. "This place offers far better security than the hotel does," Eddie said as he observed the tall walls and curling razor wire above them.

As soon as the missionary women received the word that they were moving, they began preparing. Abigail packed her backpack and heaved a plastic bag of belongings out to the vehicle, where she met Jessica by the open trunk of the box cruiser. The young woman's face was wreathed in smiles. "Abby, I found something out that you won't believe!"

"Oh?" Abigail fell into step with her younger friend on the way to the bustling hotel porch.

"We posted our missionary team photo online yesterday, and one of Allen's relatives recognized you and commented. We're related! You and Allen are second cousins."

Abigail's jaw dropped. Related to the trailblazing young doctor! "Cousins. I had no idea. What are the chances that we should unknowingly end up in the same African country at the same time?"

Jessica shook her head with a little smile. "It's pretty crazy."

Finally, as they settled themselves into the vehicles for a trip to the other side of town, everyone but the driver of each vehicle lay low to stay out of sight. Nathan and Keith also took less-traveled roads to avoid attention. Once inside the compound, Abigail breathed a little sigh of relief and marveled at the beautiful grassy meadows along the river. Several fine houses stood in a row along a gravel road, and the missionaries would be housed in the first two-bedroom house in the line.

As they began exploring the area, Shiloh twirled her dress in the breeze from the river. "Look, everyone, there's a swing on the porch!"

"This is the fanciest house I've seen in Congo," Abigail marveled and then turned to her husband in amazement. The large main room was painted bright pink, and its walls were decorated with bold African artwork. Plush couches hedged in a fuzzy white rug not far from a kitchen bar lined with tall stools. A side hallway led to two other rooms, including a master bedroom.

While the quarters appeared immense to Abigail at first, the living area grew smaller when all seventeen adults and children flooded inside. Tammy and Starla set out to babyproof the area while the Mosier kids began to tussle on the couch. The families with children each claimed a bedroom and moved their things inside, and the two couples without children were assigned to sleep in the general living area that night.

"Which would you rather have for sleeping quarters—the living room or the kitchen?" Allen asked an hour later from where he lay sprawled on the couch. He cracked open an eye as Caleb Mosier began tickling his big socked feet.

"We'll take the kitchen and the old mattress," Abigail answered, grinning.

Allen reached for Jessica's hand when she had settled on the couch nearby. "Can we take a walk down by the river?" he begged as an onslaught of Mosier children made a beeline in his direction.

Jessica laughed, in no apparent hurry to leave her photo editing project. "Oh Allen, the children would miss you too much if we left for a walk."

Allen covered his face with a pillow in feigned despair. Then, possessed with new energy, he reached for Caleb's kicking feet to tickle him in return.

"Alright now, kids, who wants to take a walk down by the river?" Keith called out. Allen jumped up from the couch in relief just as the mission president turned to him. "I've been talking with my wife and Pastor Mtenzi about visiting the campus in a few days. Don't you have some things to retrieve from the clinic building?"

Allen's expression perked up. "Provided that the items haven't been stolen, yes, I do."

"Do you want to go, Abby?" Chris turned to his wife.

Abigail's eyes widened as she slowly shook her head. "I will stay here and help with the children. Honestly, I don't feel that I have the emotional and physical energy to go." *How can I bear to see the campus drive again?* she wondered. The thought of traversing the same winding driveway where Soni's still form lay only several days before was intensely painful. Additionally, their food supply was low. Abigail carefully saved her remaining granola bars for emergencies but felt herself growing physically weaker. She detested her lack of endurance.

"Mamma Rebecca is coming tomorrow to help us," Starla told the group that evening as they finished the last of the bananas and peanuts together. "She can bring some cooked beans from campus so that we can have an actual meal."

Night fell just before a large truck roared through the gate into the compound. Loud, joyous shouts cut through the still air. With the accident so fresh on her consciousness, Abigail trembled, realizing that a large group of men was sitting in the open air of the truck bed. *Do they realize how dangerous this Congolese habit is?* She shuddered. *Someone was killed because of it. And we could have been, too, even though we had nothing to do with his decision.*

"They are championing a political party," Keith explained quietly. "The governor is already here and staying in the house next door." Then he added, "We are happy to stay out of government politics and focus on serving the people we came to reach here in Congo."

When Mamma Rebecca arrived on the compound the next morning, Starla and Abigail eagerly greeted her with hugs. Mamma Rebecca quickly busied herself around the unfamiliar kitchen and oversaw the time-consuming process of making beans edible. When the beans were finished, she set them out in a large pan on the counter. Jessica peered into the pan with surprise. "These are just plain beans. No tomato paste or seasonings."

Abigail tried a few beans on a plate. "Not even salt, it would seem."

"I'll pass for now," Jessica said as she returned to the couch.

Abigail was too hungry to care that the beans had no salt. Babysitting Shiloh and Caleb that morning had sapped what energy she had left. As she sat on a stool by the counter, she intentionally raised her arm to bring a spoonful to her mouth. *I almost feel too weak to hold up my arms now.* How thankful she was for Mamma Rebecca's beans!

Shiloh, Caleb, and Anna soon joined her in the kitchen to enjoy the plain beans. As they ate together, Abigail felt strength returning to her small frame. *Thank You, Father, for the blessing of food*, she prayed silently. *May I never take it for granted.*

Abigail wasn't the only one to struggle. She walked into the living room to see Tammy trembling on the couch.

"Are you OK?" Abigail asked quickly.

"I hope so," Tammy replied between shivers. "I think my blood sugar is low." Her hands and fingers were shaking uncontrollably.

Abigail ran for an electrolyte packet of Vitamin C—one she had found in her backpack on the day of the wild escape from campus. She poured the mixture into a cup of water and handed it to Tammy. As the missionary mother drank it down in sips, Abigail wondered if people across the world in America had any concept of what God's frontline workers persevered through. *If they could only see the numerous challenges and trials these people meet with grace*, she thought. *The missionaries suffer without a complaint. These people are heroes, consumed by a love that cannot be destroyed, and that only makes them stronger.*

Abigail began praying as soon as Keith and Tammy (who was revived and feeling normal again), Cousin Allen, and Christopher left to return to the campus. The small group was accompanied by several armed police officers for safety as they traveled again over the familiar winding road out of town. They lumbered past the motorcycle wash pond and then the houses—abandoned thanks to the local thieves—around each bend.

When Keith pulled the vehicle alongside the campus green, he could see that two of the houses in the circle had been broken into. The mob had apparently tried to set one on fire, but the flames never caught enough to burn substantially.

"Are we stopping at your house first?" Chris asked Keith from the back seat.

"That's the plan," the mission president answered as they drove in that direction.

As they approached the Mosiers' silent home, Chris stopped to inspect the side door. "The welds on your steel gate are broken," he remarked, then stepped up into the house. The Mosiers' home had always been a beacon of hospitality and Christian love. Now, as Christopher walked over the cement floors, the damage done by the thieves was visible. The kitchen cupboards were bare, and Keith's guitar was no longer hanging on the wall. Dirty shoe prints marred the couple's bed, now stripped of its comforter and sheets.

"The set of pans we were given at our wedding is gone," Tammy remarked as she looked up from an empty cabinet.

"They are replaceable," Keith said gently. Even a stripped home could not suppress his characteristic optimism. "Prence and the others *did* do us one favor—the chest freezer and refrigerator are completely emptied. That's one less thing to worry about."

"True," Tammy nodded.

Christopher left to search his own house, leaving Keith and Tammy to throw what clothes they could find into a duffel bag. "The printing container looks untouched," he noted as he passed by the Rittenours' home.

The lone American felt his heart swelling with emotion as he jogged up the driveway path in the drizzling rain. So much had changed. The warm family atmosphere of the mission had dissipated, and in its place, police guards stood armed with AK-47s by the porch of every building. Chris spoke into the jungle: "The devil will not triumph!" Only the quiet patter of rain greeted his ears.

A policeman in blue, sporting an AK-47 and a grenade launcher, stood outside the Dumans' porch. The law enforcement officer silently watched as Chris unlocked the steel gate, then he followed the tall missionary under the awning of the porch to watch him pack.

It was immediately obvious that the mob had left his home untouched. Once inside, Chris worked quickly. He tried not to feel overwhelmed by the conglomerate of items thrown inside from the porch as he worked his way toward the bedroom and retrieved as many things as he could.

The sound of a vehicle outside on the lawn arrested Christopher's attention. It was Allen, who jumped out of the box cruiser. "Let me help you load," he said as he bounded across the porch and reached for a suitcase Chris had packed. Together, they locked the house again and swung back by the Mosier home to pick up Keith and Tammy. With mixed emotions, the group left the campus behind and set off down the road to Kisangani.

The Mosier children rejoiced when their parents arrived back safely, and

Abigail ran to give Christopher a hug. Tammy quickly changed into a fresh set of clothes and returned with a familiar outfit. "That skirt and top look beautiful on you, Tammy," Abigail complimented her. "I don't know why my clothes look so much better on other people than they do on me."

"Oh, that's not true!" Tammy laughed, scooping up Talitha, who tugged on her skirt.

Abigail smiled to see that Tammy seemed happier. Maybe her visit to the campus, unsettling as it was, had brought some closure. After all, even though many of their belongings had been stolen, they were together as a family and unharmed.

Abigail sorted through the items Christopher recovered from campus and tucked a pile away for Kayumba and his family. "Maybe these bandannas will cheer the hearts of his boys," she said hopefully.

Chris hadn't brought all of their possessions back with him due to limited time. Their headlamps still lay under their pillows on the beautiful African comforter. Their Swahili songbooks sat in the bookcase by the wall—where Abigail's blue journal also rested. It would probably sit until it molded in the tropical humidity. But at this point, it really didn't matter. Abigail reflected on the events of the last few months, remembering how she had shared God's blessings with her fellow missionaries and locals. She was incredibly glad that she had given and that her blessings could be shared before the day of the accident. She never felt so thankful for life and for the privilege of enjoying another day—with or without her things.

CHAPTER 20

SUNSET ON THE CONGO

Their pleasant accommodations by the Congo River lasted for several weeks as the missionaries lingered and prayed for the future of the mission. Seeing that the city remained unsettled and the campus was unsafe, each family reached the general consensus that a return to America was in order. Keith expected that it would be temporary. "We will reevaluate and try to return again in the spring when the political situation has settled down again," he explained.

At greater ease now, surrounded by the tall walls, the adults enjoyed a small vacation. They watched little Daniel and the Mosier kids frolic in the lush grass, and many an evening, overlooking the Congo, they traced the journey of riverboats on the horizon. Their Muslim host was stout—a jovial Indian man, who looked pleased as he gave the families a tour of a massive house-building project on the other side of the compound.

"He must be extremely wealthy," Abigail whispered to Chris as they gazed from a third-story window of the house shell. "This place will be a mansion when he's through with it, and the view is already amazing." The lawn below was brilliant green and bordered by solid fencing. Sunlight glinted across the deep waters of the Congo not far beyond.

"Did you hear that we are invited to a dinner this evening on the lawn?" Chris asked, touching her arm. "I don't know if the governor will be there, but it sounds like it will be pretty nice." When they rejoined Keith and their host downstairs on the main level, the couple caught a few words of their conversation.

"Everyone knows that accidents happen," the Indian spoke reassuringly. "Accidents are costly and even dangerous to people like us. That's why I have walls and guards for protection."

Upon returning to their rented guest house, Abigail saw that Starla and Tammy had organized a semblance of a schedule with the little ones. Ever loyal, Mamma Rebecca had taken a moto-taxi through Kisangani to help with food preparation again, and she had already busied herself around the kitchen, humming in low tones. Quietly, the young American woman approached her.

"I am returning to America tomorrow," Abigail said as she slipped off her watch. "Please take this as my gift to you."

As Mamma Rebecca gave her an embrace, a lump caught in the younger woman's throat. Rebecca immediately slipped the familiar watch around her own wrist and washed dishes at the sink with a lingering smile as Anna Mosier prattled in Swahili.

The dinner provided by their Muslim host was a well-prepared event. Helpers set up tables and chairs under an awning on the lawn. A young Indian in trendy jeans set up a sound system, which began to roar American pop music as a small group of upper-class Kisangani residents lingered around the grounds. The Muslim seemed especially pleased by the presence of his American guests, and the missionaries were served with a wonderful array of food. Each table was graced with a bowl of seasoned chips, and sodas in ice-cold glass bottles accompanied each place setting.

Abigail had never seen this facet of Congo life. "It's as if I've been transported to a different world," she marveled. *Maybe this is a taste of what Belgian Congo was like, back when it provided a lavish way of life for the wealthy upper class.* She remembered the ghost town along the way to Isangi. Maybe it had looked something like this compound at one point, only on a much larger scale.

This scene on the lawn beside the Congo River reminded her somewhat of the American landscape of plenty. If she squeezed her eyes shut, she could almost forget about the poverty outside the walls where beggars haunted the streets and people lived with little more than a few clothes and cooking pans. But no matter how beautiful and safe she felt now, she couldn't forget what lay beyond: the faces of her Congolese friends outside the tall compound walls were indelibly etched in her memory.

The English music blared. In efforts to avoid the intensity of the secular songs, Abigail played hide-and-seek with the missionary children on the lawn. Several Muslim little ones joined Shiloh as she dashed behind a lemon bush. Abigail looked up to see a familiar figure standing by the yard entrance. The woman's hair was wrapped in familiar, worn cloth, and her calloused hands fell awkwardly at her sides.

It was Mamma Rebecca. The sun had begun its downward trend in the sky, and Abigail realized that the woman must leave soon to safely make the trek to campus. Rebecca waved but remained at the fence gate as if an invisible line prevented her from ever daring to enter. Mamma Rebecca keenly felt the distinctness of the invisible boundary. She stood in the shadow of a mansion but could not allow herself to set foot on the lush grass.

Abigail approached. *Oh, Mamma Rebecca, I would cross this invisible line from my world of comfort and security a thousand times for your sake. It is why I am here.*

"Are you returning home?" Abigail asked as she approached. "*Nyumbani* [home]?"

The Congolese woman nodded, taking the American's hand in hers. A stream of Swahili poured from her lips. Abigail couldn't understand it any better than on the day of the accident when she called out on the road. But the feeling in her voice and emotion in her gaze said enough. The two women embraced. This was goodbye for who knew how long.

"*Mungu bariki saana.*" Abigail swallowed a lump in her throat. "God bless you so very much, Mamma Rebecca."

She bowed her head. "Nathan and Starla—could you get them for me?" Her eyes skimmed over the lingering figures on the lawn and lighted on the little family she lovingly worked for.

Abigail nodded and then walked to the large tent where the Rittenours still sat. When Abigail explained that Mamma Rebecca was leaving, Nathan and Starla came quickly to the little gate where their worker stood. Starla and Rebecca instantly melted into tears and then parted with kind words of friendship. The missionaries had taken leave to America on numerous occasions before, but somehow this parting felt different.

The missionaries retired from the party and gathered together in their cottage for evening worship. Chris's guitar had survived the great ordeal on campus, and Keith smiled as his fingers touched the strings. "I'll have to pick up another guitar when I'm back in the States," Keith said cheerfully.

Abigail scanned the faces of her friends, who felt more like family now. Her gaze fell on Allen, reminding her that one friend actually *was* family. This felt like old times, when on many nights, they gathered in the Mosiers' living room to sing, dream, and plan for the future.

"Children, I'm going to sing you a song," Keith said softly.

Jessica sat near Allen on the couch, her arm linked with his and a thoughtful expression on her face. Talitha chirped from Tammy's lap, blond hair falling in waves across her tiny forehead. Caleb and Shiloh squirmed, cross-legged on the floor, peering into the face of their daddy hero. Chris and Abby stood nearby, watching the scene in the living room with a sense of peace. Just outside the window, Nathan and Starla sat with Daniel on the swing, conversing with Kayumba in the faint breeze.

"Come here, Anna." Keith beckoned to his three-year-old.

"I'm here, Daddy," her little voice lisped.

"Are you my happy girl this evening?"

"Yes, Daddy." A shy smile suddenly burst across her little face.

He pulled her close for a moment. Then, with a lingering light in his eyes, the mission leader began to sing.

"The golden morning is fast approaching;
    Jesus soon will come
To take His faithful and happy children
    To their promised home.

O, we see the gleams of the golden morning
    Piercing through this night of gloom!
Oh, we see the gleams of the golden morning
    That will burst the tomb."[1]

The emotion of his gentle, melodic voice spoke of dreams for Congo. For all of Africa. For the whole world. The words were touching when Keith sang them two months ago, but they carried a much more personal element on this day. They spoke of faith and courage in the face of death and discouraging times. They recognized that God gave each of His children a window of time in which to work for Him and that the gleams of a golden morning in heaven were at the door.

"I will miss these wonderful times together." Abigail broke the silence at the close of the song.

Allen Smith turned from his seat on the couch, alerted to her presence. "Oh, hey, cuz." He grinned mischievously.

"I still can't believe that we're related." She smiled with a little shake of her head.

"This is only a taste of what it will be like in heaven," Tammy ventured. "Where we're all family and safe forever from the devil."

Alvina entered the room just then, phone in hand. "I just heard from my boys in the States," she announced, beaming. "They are relieved to hear of God's miracles on our behalf over the past week."

"We continue to pray for them, Alvina," Starla assured her mother-in-law.

"I pray for them too—every morning, rain or shine." A wonderful smile graced the grandmother's face as she retired for the night.

"I'm sad that Mamma Mtenzi isn't here anymore," Shiloh piped up from where she was now balanced on Keith's knee.

"Mamma Mtenzi is happy to see her sons in Tanzania right now, Shiloh," Tammy prompted from her seat on the floor. "She will come back."

Remembering the bag she had previously packed for Kayumba and his family, Abigail walked to the porch where he and the Rittenours talked. The evening air was growing cool, and crickets chirped in the guest house crevices.

"Hi, Abby." Kayumba extended a hand as she approached.

After returning his greeting, Abigail held out the bag. "I want Kayumba to know that these are for him and his family," she said looking to Nathan, who translated.

"*Asante* Mamma," Kayumba murmured as he reached for the bag. "Thank you."

Again, she wished that she could express to him what a treasure he was to God's heart, to the mission, and to all of the families who served there. *Few could find a truer friend. How strange that here, in this foreign land where I could have lost my life due to bitter enemies, I have also found the most loyal friends.*

Kayumba turned to Nathan. "The village of Huit knows that the death was an accident," he said. "Everything will be OK. My friends and I have begun a prayer group, where all the Adventist churches in town are praying for the continuing of God's work and for our missionary friends to be of good courage."

Nathan nodded. "Thank you, Kayumba."

The Congolese continued. "The devil has not won the battle. I believe that truth will triumph in the end. No matter what the future holds, God's work will continue."

He can always send His angels to Kisangani again, Abigail thought as she listened.

Pastor Mtenzi stood on the gravel path when Kayumba turned to leave. The Congolese swung his leg over a motorcycle taxi, and then, slowly, he rolled into the dusty streets of Kisangani and disappeared from sight. "There goes a changed man," Mtenzi said. The sparkle of light in the Tanzanian's dark eyes had rekindled.

"It changes a man to face death," Chris agreed as they returned to the porch. Abigail gazed at her husband quietly as he spoke. At that moment, she knew Kayumba wasn't the only one who had experienced such a change.

This was the missionaries' final evening together as a team. The party was over, but the sun had not yet sunk below the horizon. The families lingered once more by the river. Together, they stood at the fence and watched the children romp again in the green grass. The view was grand, overlooking a steep descent to the deep waters below.

As Keith looked out over the mighty Congo River, he spoke as if deep in thought. "We must reach the point in life where our fear of God is greater than our fear of men."

Shiloh, Caleb, and Anna scampered over the thick grass nearby. The sound of lighthearted laughter echoed back from the tall compound's walls. Jessica and Allen reclined on the grassy turf, looking up into the wide expanse of the African sky.

"Here's a flower for you, Miss Jessica," Anna said, grinning.

"Why, I love it," the woman physician exclaimed as she cupped the petals between her soft, tanned fingers.

"Nathan." Abigail turned to him as he pulled Daniel up onto his shoulders. "I want the materials I printed to go out to the locals. Whether the campus becomes a safe place again or not, the printed word will continue to speak for us."

Nathan nodded. "I feel the same way. We will make sure that the booklets are distributed."

"It would be a shame for the well at the Barry Mosier School to remain unfinished," Chris interjected as he thought of his own project.

"Kayumba can finish the well," Nathan said. "I gave him instructions earlier today, and he knows where to find the tools. We can trust him to do a good job."

The young man looked relieved but only partially satisfied.

Abigail read his thoughts. "God is not limited to us to complete His work." She tucked her thin fingers into his large, warm hand. "We are only a small piece of a great puzzle to bring the gospel to the whole world. Whether we live or die, what matters is that we are faithful to His call."

A faint hint of a smile etched his lips. "You've come a long way since you first came to campus and learned about the robbers."

She laughed softly. "I suppose I have. It's been quite a journey."

A sunset of peach and pink streaked across the sky. Several dugouts hugged the bank below as a thin line of smoke traveled up through the dense tree canopy across the wide river. A large boat chugged slowly downstream, sending tiny waves lapping against the winding shoreline.

Christopher tracked the flight of a bird with his eyes as it made wide circles in the fading twilight. "Honestly, I don't know what our future holds, and I don't understand all that God sees fit to allow," He mused aloud.

"The day of the accident feels like a distant nightmare," Abigail added as she ran her hand over the stone wall between them and the steep river bank. "It's as if our escape from the mob took place in a different world."

"In a way, it was a different world, Abby. A very different one than what our Indian friend has in this lavish compound, safely guarded by men and razor wire."

"I'd rather be guarded by angels," his wife interjected.

Chris looked at her knowingly. "You know what it looks like outside of these walls."

She nodded. "Dirty streets and impoverished people."

"As life takes us to different places, this is a lesson we can't allow ourselves to forget: No matter how secure and beautiful our bubble is, we must remember the people who live outside. People like Kayumba, and Mamma Rebecca, and even vengeful Prence—people who might never have the opportunity to see the power of God's love in action if we never cared enough to go, to share, and to give."

"That's a beautiful thought." She sighed peacefully as she savored this last view of the African sunset over the river. She knew that if God had called her to live and die on this hard-packed ground in the Democratic Republic of Congo, she would have been willing. But at that moment, her heart over-flowed with gratitude for the life that she had surrendered and for the life the Lord had given her back again.

"No." She turned to Christopher as evening shadows lengthened across the Congo's rippling waters. "We will never forget."

---

1. S. J. Graham, "Gleams of the Golden Morning" (1900).

EPILOGUE

Sunlight streamed through the dense, tropical woodlands of Kisangani as a pair of African grey parrots cackled in morning song.

A lone figure ambled around the corner of Nathan Rittenour's empty house. In a past era on the mission campus, one often saw this Congolese worker reporting for the day's duties at the doorstep. Nathan would emerge from the doorway with little golden-haired Daniel in his arms, and the child's face would be graced with a goatee of guava-banana smoothie.

But now, the house stood empty. In the short space of one morning—November 1, 2017, when a tragic accident forced the Americans to leave—the campus was transformed from a cheerful and bustling nest of American missionaries to a handful of shaken but faith-filled Congolese. They were left facing all the devil's rage and wondering what would happen next.

Pastor Mtenzi strolled the campus grounds now, taking a break from his frequent work in the office where he coordinated evangelism efforts. As he approached the Rittenour place, the sound of a man's voice blended with the noise of morning birds. Curious, he drew near.

Kayumba stood behind the empty house, dressed in his jeans and cotton T-shirt. His face tilted upward as he spoke into the broad expanse of blue above.

"I found Kayumba behind Nathan's house today," Msifiri Mtenzi wrote to his friends in the United States that afternoon. "He was practicing preaching. I arranged for him to speak at the Adventist church in Huit, and his message was a blessing. He is a changed man."

By Christmas of that year, all the American missionary families had returned to the United States. A politically turbulent election in DRC brought unrest to Kisangani for longer than expected when the Congolese president refused to leave office. In February 2018, hundreds of protesting locals were dispersed by flying bullets and tear gas canisters. Several were injured.

Despite political tensions, the church the missionaries had left behind flourished. Although some branches of the mission closed, Pastor and Mrs.

EPILOGUE

Mtenzi worked tirelessly in evangelism, renting quarters from the kind Muslim man along the Congo River's edge while laboring on campus by day. Many of the mission workers were laid off due to decreased funds, but the mission continued to support Kayumba, Leon the guard, and trained Bible workers across many parts of Congo. One year after the deadly accident, over a thousand Congolese were baptized and became Seventh-day Adventists—a number greater than in any one year since the mission began.

Kayumba continued to work as an advocate for the missionaries, helping save the campus from being destroyed on several occasions when hired police guards stirred up trouble in cooperation with the local mafia.

Although the American missionaries planned to return to the Kisangani campus to continue their mission work, the dream never materialized. Keith and Barry placed the mission campus into the hands of the local Adventist conference so evangelism could continue. Most of the missionaries' belongings remaining on the campus, including the large well-drilling rig, were sold to benefit Bible workers and further bless the Congolese. Congo Frontline Missions reconfigured to become Africa Frontline Missions as the missionaries scattered to other African countries.

The campus in Kisangani grew increasingly unsafe with the threats of robbery and other crimes. A few years after the campus was closed, Pastor Mtenzi felt that he had done all that he could. The Mtenzis relocated to labor for the gospel in their homeland of Tanzania. Allen and Jessica encountered closed doors when they endeavored to plant a hospital in Congo, so they set their sights on other places. Keith and Tammy Mosier served in the country of Chad for several years before returning to the United States. As for Nathan, Starla, and Daniel, they remained in the States to welcome a second child—a little girl—before also moving to Tanzania to serve. Alvina remained in the United States, enjoying much-needed rest and recuperation from the challenges experienced in the DRC. The quiet woman experienced many answers to her heartfelt prayers.

As for the novice missionary recruits, Christopher and Abigail Duman, they remained in the States and became involved in one of the few Seventh-day Adventist nonprofit organizations in DRC, based in Congo's capital, Kinshasa. Managed by a dedicated Congolese pastor, Train Them 2 Fish continues to train and support Bible workers, conduct free medical clinics, and carry evangelistic series to communities searching for truth. The myriad challenges faced years ago by Congo Frontline Missions in Kisangani are also a continual reality for Train Them 2 Fish. Nevertheless, God continues to work, sending His angels to the Congolese people with messages of direction and hope.

As for the churches planted by Congo Frontline Missions and the congregations that surround the Kisangani area, it is reported that many are flourishing. Kayumba and many of the other local workers have not forgotten their American friends. Each pursues God's calling on their lives. They continue to exhibit the same faith that graced their efforts on the day of the deadly accident that put their Christianity to the test. The witness and testimony from a small cluster of missionary families were only to be for a time and a season—and God knew it from the beginning.

The story of the final events at Kisangani leading up to November 1, 2017, serves as a poignant reminder that time is short. As God's people prepare to face the final days of earth's history, they are given a limited amount of time to work before the doors close. While sometimes facing fearful circumstances, those who seek God and cling to Him in times of trouble will find faith and courage enough to bear a true testimony. Eternity—where friends are family and love prevails—awaits the faithful in heavenly courts above.